Command and Control in the Information Age

James Moffat is a Fellow of Dstl, a Fellow of Operational Research, and a Visiting Professor at the University of Cranfield. In 2000 he was awarded the President's Medal of the Operational Research Society for his work on ASTOR (the Airborne Stand-off Radar system). In this book he describes in detail the results of his research in representing military command, control, sensing and situation assessment, in fast-running agent-based computer models of conflict. These approaches are at the basis of a new generation of models that will help to significantly shape future defence policy and expenditure.

Command and Control in the Information Age
Representing its Impact

James Moffat
Policy and Capability Studies Department
The Defence Science and Technology Laboratory

London: TSO

Published by TSO (The Stationery Office) and available from:

Online
www.tso.co.uk/bookshop

Mail, Telephone, Fax & E-mail
TSO
PO Box 29, Norwich, NR3 1GN
Telephone orders/General enquiries: 0870 600 5522
Fax orders: 0870 600 5533
E-mail: book.orders@tso.co.uk
Textphone 0870 240 3701

TSO Shops
123 Kingsway, London, WC2B 6PQ
020 7242 6393 Fax 020 7242 6394
68-69 Bull Street, Birmingham B4 6AD
0121 236 9696 Fax 0121 236 9699
9-21 Princess Street, Manchester M60 8AS
0161 834 7201 Fax 0161 833 0634
16 Arthur Street, Belfast BT1 4GD
028 9023 8451 Fax 028 9023 5401
18-19 High Street, Cardiff CF10 1PT
029 2039 5548 Fax 029 2038 4347
71 Lothian Road, Edinburgh EH3 9AZ
0870 606 5566 Fax 0870 606 5588

TSO Accredited Agents
(see Yellow Pages)

and through good booksellers

ISBN 011 772984 1

This book is dedicated to my wife Jacqueline, and my children Louise and Katherine, without whose support and understanding it would not have been written.

James Moffat, July 2001

Contents

List of figures

List of tables

Abbreviations

AI	artificial intelligence
AO	area of operations
BDI	beliefs, desires and intentions
CAS	complex adaptive systems
C2	command and control
C2W	command and control warfare
CCE	close combat entity
CoA	courses of action
CSS	combat service support
DLM	dynamic linear model
DoD	US Department of Defense
DRAW-D	defend, reinforce, attack, withdraw and delay
ECIs	enemy capabilities and intentions
GA	genetic algorithm
MoE	measures of effectiveness
NDM	naturalistic decision-making
OA	operational analysis
OPSEC	operational security
PCPR	perceived combat power ratio
ROC	receiver operating characteristic
RP	recognised picture
RPD	recognition-primed decision
RPDM	recognition-primed decision-making
SA	situation awareness
SOC	self-organised criticality

Preface

For many years, the study of military command and control (including all the associated processes such as intelligence gathering and situation assessment) was placed in the 'too difficult' box. This led to a number of significant problems. Since command and control could not be properly represented or its benefits quantified, it was difficult to argue the case for more information resources rather than simply more front-line forces. Perhaps this did not matter so much during the Cold War, when such command processes were rather stylised and scripted. However, in the new era we now inhabit, Cold War certainties have been replaced by a rich set of complex trajectories into the future: for example, asymmetric effects between information age and industrial or agricultural age opponents, as tragically demonstrated on 11 September 2001 in New York and Washington DC.

Command and control is now seen as central to the enterprise of conflict. In dynamical terms, it could be argued that we have moved from the linear regime to the region of complexity – and we need to know how to manage such complexity.

In this book I have set out a method for addressing such issues which should help us to understand and analyse the implications of this shift of perspective through the exploitation of ideas drawn from the 'new sciences' of artificial intelligence, complexity and catastrophe. Perhaps, in doing so, we can gain a deeper understanding not only of conflict but also of the avoidance of conflict, which is the ultimate aim of the political/military art.

I would like to take the opportunity here to thank everyone I have worked with along the way. All their contributions are duly acknowledged in the text, I hope.

The work, of course, is not finished. In the final chapter I have indicated some 'paths to the future' that I plan to roam along in the next few years.

James Moffat
Defence Science and Technology Laboratory

Note to reader

Many of the references cited in this book are unpublished Dstl reports. These may be obtained from Dstl Knowledge Services via the following e-mail address: ksglasgow@dstl.gov.uk.

Figures 4.4, 4.5 and 4.6 are reprinted from Smith, J Q, Harrison, P J and Zeeman, E C, 'The analysis of some discontinuous decision processes', *European Journal of Operational Research*, Vol. 7, pp. 30–43 (1981), with permission granted by Elsevier Science.

The cover shows a screen shot of one of the testbeds being used to develop the algorithms that represent the human decision-making process of military command. It shows a campaign-level Land/Air interaction between two forces (Reds and Blue) in which Red, using a bold command strategy developed by a genetic algorithm, fixes Blue in the South and then flanks North to exploit a hole in Blue's defence. The boxes with a single diagonal line are airborne sensors that help to generate the operational picture and assessment of enemy intent on which the plan is based.

1
Context

In this book, I want to talk about the way in which future command and control can be described, and captured in computer simulation models of conflict, when applied to warfare in the 'information age'. This has been a long-standing challenge for operational analysis (the defence application of operational research). However, by drawing on agent-based approaches, progress can be made. We start here by setting the scene, and explaining in particular why we use the phrase 'information age'. The following account is drawn from a paper published in the *Journal of Defence Science* [1] and helps to set a context for our thinking.

In all that follows, the plain English term command and control (abbreviated to C2) is used to describe all the activities associated with the military command process, including sensing, intelligence, data fusion, decision-making, etc. I would like to acknowledge here the contribution of Professor Gwyn Prins, London School of Economics, to the discussion in this chapter.

Introduction

In considering the great transformations that followed the ending of the Cold War, I was involved in exploring two dimensions of transformation that affect the potential futures for the military art. One was the impact of new risk environments and complex pathways of causation in social/political affairs on the task of modelling, viewed as an important aspect of decision support. The other was to consider whether the 'revolution in military affairs' included new ideas which should cause us to change our way of thinking about the military aspects of security in a similarly revolutionary manner. To this end, a number of seminars organised by Professor Prins and myself addressed questions of modelling and the impact of the revolution in military affairs upon military thinking.

The first seminar was given by Dr Geoff Jenkins, who directs the development and employment of the Earth Systems Model being built at the Hadley Centre for Climate Prediction and Research within the UK Meteorological Office. The second, by Peter Grainger of the Ministry of Defence, reviewed many of the different types of models employed within operational analysis, and was commented upon by Professor Stephen Watson from the Management School at Lancaster University. The third seminar was addressed by Dr David Alberts of the Office of the Secretary of Defense, DoD, USA, and introduced thinking which tends towards the view that the revolution in military affairs does indeed imply commensurate change in strategic thought. It was commented upon by the present author (JM). The final seminar was introduced by Major-General Alastair Irwin, then Commandant, the Royal Military College of Science (RMCS), who looked at the whole question of the so-called revolution in military affairs from a practitioner's perspective.

What follows is a series of reflections on the complex issues that arose from that seminar series.

Four key questions

The seminars uncovered four key questions, which move from the entirely technical to the deeply political. Three of these questions were explicitly discussed in the seminars; the fourth was implicit, but is raised here, not least because circumstances in the Balkans forced it to the fore.

The four questions are:

1   Will the entry of the technologies of the information age into military affairs reduce the fog of war, or not?
2   What may be the implications of answers to question 1 for the future conduct of command in war?
3   What do the answers to questions 1 and 2 imply for the development of models ('best guess') and technology choices ('best bet') appropriate to the future shape of conflict?
4   If (as on present trends seems probable) the USA invests heavily in network-centric warfare technologies and supporting regimes, what may be the political, strategic and operational implications for the rest of us?

Question 1: Will the entry of the technologies of the information age into military affairs reduce the fog of war, or not?

In his recent book David Alberts, Office of the Secretary of Defense at the Pentagon, has placed the concept of 'network-centric warfare' at the core of what the future of war might look like [2]. The essential idea is that of a force structure which allows the 'bottom-up' self-synchronisation of autonomous units in the battlespace, in order to achieve specific mission objectives. These objectives are recognised through a shared awareness that all units have of the situation and of the overall goals to be achieved. What are the key drivers that have led him to this conclusion?

First, he is impressed by Alvin Toffler's argument that modern civilisation has gone through three 'ages' [3]. Toffler calls these the agricultural age, the machine age and the information age.

The first of these was facilitated by the neolithic agricultural revolution which domesticated animals and plants; the second by the industrial revolution, which harnessed steam and steel; and the third by the computer revolution, which has transformed the assemblage and processing of information. Toffler also points out that in each age warfare has been waged using the technology existing or emerging at that time. We moved from spears and arrows to guns, and are now moving from kinetic to non-kinetic forms of warfare, for as we move from the machine age into the information age the same is true for us as it was for our forebears. Thus, Alberts asserts, the key technology for future warfare is the management of information.

The second key driver was initiated by the fall of the Berlin Wall. As we continue to peer through the dust of its collapse, the disintegration of the Soviet Union, and subsequent events, what we see is not one future but a range of possible futures, characterised by uncertainty. This military uncertainty mirrors the economic uncertainty engendered by sharply interacting market-based economies.

From the commercial perspective, the reaction to such economic uncertainties has been to adopt institutional structures which are much more flexible, and adaptive to change. We have moved from the Dickensian hierarchy, where Bob Cratchit sat and shivered on his scribe's stool at the bottom of the heap, to the informed network (the flat management structure). Commerce too has been swept along by the forces identified by Toffler, and information is the glue that holds the future company together. We can see this happening in the use of company-wide intranet services by organisations such as Shell and IBM, which span the globe.

Driven by the same underlying forces of increasing global uncertainty and transition to the information age, it is not surprising that the armed forces should consider more loosely based federations of functions to perform a mission in a self-synchronous way. This seems to be the essence of the network-centric approach. In this sense, the armed forces are not copying the commercial world: they are merely reacting in a similar way to similar forces of change. Flat command structures to maximise agility and force flexibility in response to the transition to the information age and uncertainty can be seen as inevitable from this perspective.

Figure 1.1: The command cycle

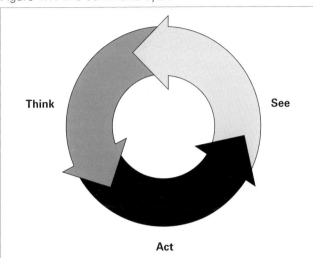

Consider the command cycle shown in Figure 1.1 Clausewitzian warfare is about coping with fog and friction. We are limited by what we can perceive and what actions are available to us in reaction to these perceptions. 'Fog' delimits our perception (through limits in our sensors or fusion processes, or through deliberate enemy deception). Friction constrains the number of courses of action open to us in response to our perception of events. The aim of network-centric and similar philosophies is to lift fog and friction, thus allowing command to cycle more quickly, leading to the desired force agility and flexibility. However, discussion of this during the seminar series indicates that there are also potentially very severe disadvantages to such a development, which have to be addressed. For example:

- Such structures could be fragile rather than robust. They may be vulnerable to single-point failures of the digitised battlespace (e.g. denial of satellite support).
- The assumption that the system is all-seeing could lead to arrogance, repeating the errors of Vietnam and Kosovo. In both cases, what was perceived to be going on in the battlefield, either through body counts in Vietnam or through sensor footage of tanks being destroyed in Kosovo, might be a very distorted picture of what is actually being achieved.

- Dehumanisation of war, and increased use of stand-off systems, sensor networks and robotics may lead to warfare which is beyond civilised rules [4].
- The ultimate extreme of this approach is the complete fusion of sensor and shooter in unmanned warfare – this could be perceived as a pointless activity [4].
- With such flat command structures it may be difficult to force the issue, tell soldiers to go in harm's way and motivate people to fight.

Question 2: What may be the implications of answers to question 1 for the future conduct of command in war?

We have already argued that, from the perspective of the key drivers of transition to the information age and increased structural uncertainty, such network-centric-based structures could be seen as inevitable – a vision of the future which is unavoidable. However, there are alternative futures in which this does not occur, either because of the downside effects (some of which we have discussed) or because it may be pointless to be a peerless information-age force in a world full of machine age or agricultural age adversaries. Asymmetric effects between adversaries in different 'ages' might lead to a balance of advantage to the adversary (through the attack of infrastructure assets such as stock exchanges, banks and logistic computer systems).

Thus if fog and friction are still key components of the future military art, then the emphasis shifts to the qualities of the *commander* (the 'think' part of the 'see–think–act' command cycle). Such commanders must be able to fuse information from a great variety of sources (political and military), particularly in messy diplomatic/military operations, in order to achieve a true sense of what is going on. An example of this was the ability of NATO commanders to undermine leadership of warring factions in Bosnia by exploiting both direct sensor information, and much more indirect cultural and political information (see also the reference to 'reading the opponent's mind' in [4]). Ultimately, any command process is a combination of such top-down command, and the 'bottom-up' effect of tactical reaction to immediate events.

Our research indicates that it is useful to consider any possible command structure as a combination of these two effects, and that it is possible to characterise them respectively as *analytical* and *naturalistic* modes of command [5]. The top-down analytical mode corresponds to the careful weighing up of alternative courses of action, based on perceptions of opposing courses of action. What this means is that, in this case, there is time to conduct such a review of possible courses of action. This review is driven by perceptions of the opponent's courses of action and a corresponding perceived set of pay-offs. Of course the opponent also has such a set of perceptions of his own. Thus, in sum, each side is driven by a set of perceived pay-offs, based on perceptions of the opposing likely courses of action. The bottom-up reaction to immediate effects is based on time-pressured and high-stress 'naturalistic decision-making processes'. This means that the effect of such stress on expert decision-makers leads to a mode of decision-making that is satisficing (that is, looking for the first acceptable solution, rather than an optimal one). The process is one of pattern-matching, in which the commander attempts to match his perception of the pattern of events to a set of stored patterns built up by experience and training. Each of these stored patterns corresponds to a course of action (a mission for the forces under his command) which is chosen from a small number of mission alternatives. Network-centric warfare could be seen as an extreme example of this process in which the bottom-up effects dominate the emergent behaviour of the system. In practice, a judicious balance between the two effects may be a more robust and useful structure.

Question 3: What do the answers to questions 1 and 2 imply for the development of models ('best guess') and technology choices ('best bet') appropriate to the future shape of conflict?

The challenge to those seeking to provide robust decision support through modelling is simply stated. Whereas during the Cold War the issue boundary was sharply delineated by the military definition of Cold War confrontation, that is no longer the case today. More so, the nature of the risk environment within which the UK exists is now changed, and considerably more complicated and multifaceted. In consequence, the likelihood of complex and unexpected interactions, arising from previously unexpected sources, is greatly increased. This point was explored in the analysis context at a workshop organised by the author in 1998 [6].

This workshop began with position papers from Professor Peter Allen of Cranfield University, Professor Michael Pidd of Lancaster University and Professor Gwyn Prins of the London School of Economics. These helped shape the discussion, identifying the value of more exploratory analysis, using simpler and smaller models. The perspectives of complexity theory and agent-based modelling were also considered to be valuable, not least because of their ability to help the customer group discard and refine models quickly when their inappropriateness became evident.

However, the issue of complexity is one that is not unique to the modelling of 'man in the loop' systems; it is the predominant characteristic of very large, coupled and integrated dynamic models of natural processes. Of these, by far the largest successful example is the coupled global-systems model already mentioned, which is being constructed at the Hadley Centre (the UK centre for climate modelling). This shows that it is possible to deal with very considerable degrees of uncertainty about the coupled impact of physical phenomena in a systematic way, which, over time, increases confidence in reliability of the model's predictions. This is done by two means: the detail and resolution in the model is progressively increased, and the model is successfully 'calibrated' by comparing it with historic data.

The key question for operational analysis (OA), however, is whether there is any useful analogy to be drawn from this success in modelling natural phenomena to the tasks now facing those modelling interactions of human will and physical systems in military operations. Human reaction could not be modelled directly in the Hadley model. However, it was taken into account indirectly because the consequences of human reaction could be observed and included. Examples quoted were rates of chlorofluorocarbon emissions or the number and density of contrails produced by jet aircraft in the stratosphere. None the less, a difficulty for the future development of this type of model arises from this inability because, in the carbon dioxide global budget, for example, human decisions drive the process. So, they cannot safely be ignored but, equally, they cannot be easily addressed.

This problem is one with which any form of economic modelling begins. Large, coupled economic models look superficially similar to the Hadley Centre Earth Systems Model. Yet they are not, because they are built on assumptions about human behaviour that are open to challenge. For example, not everyone manifestly acts as a single-minded profit maximiser. A change in the main underlying assumptions about human behaviour (in particular, human decision-making) can entirely change the outcome of an economic model, and thence comes its fragility.

On the other hand, the unique experience of combat is one in which the drive for survival in the face of mortal threat may, paradoxically, produce a degree of standardisation in human behaviour – maybe the only one (and even then, open to special cases of madly altruistic self-sacrifice by VC-winners and others) upon which we can rely. Yet the realm into which OA is being invited, of messy diplomatic/military operations, is one where that sort of assumption is decreasingly safe – a further paradox – because the contexts are less and less those of modelling mortal combat [7].

Accordingly, the virtues of agent-based architectures in models and the potential of work such as that pioneered at the Brookings Institute by the agent-based modelling group there, are seen by some to be less vulnerable to the criticisms which those who favour a narrow focus in OA direct at those who are willing to explore a wider focus. Indeed, the conventional polarity between 'soft' and 'hard' operational research is increasingly unhelpful.

The objective in these cases is not prediction in the hard science sense, any more than the method is open to successful depersonalisation. The object is to produce the best guess about the dynamic and direction of future trends, if possible with indications of likely elephant traps ahead. The methodology needs to be able to take account of the increasing centrality of the analysis of command – which means the thinking of commanders – moving into the new post–Cold War context of diplomatic/military operations.

The value of producing appropriate types of modelling, with C2 at the core of this representation, is thus seen to be central, because it is the essential precursor to being able to make the 'best bets' about where, in terms of concrete investments in new technologies, the emphasis should be placed. That technology, in all its potential forms, will need to be assessed against a view of the shape of future conflict, which cannot be either deduced in the abstract or simply assumed. The danger of assumption is one of the key issues discussed as a result of the fourth question.

Question 4: If (as on present trends seems probable) the USA invests heavily in network-centric warfare technologies and supporting regimes, what may be the political, strategic and operational implications for the rest of us?

Implicit in discussion of all three questions reviewed above is this fourth. Significant pressure exists in the USA to promote the making of considerable investments in the concept and practice of network-centric warfare. What might be the implications of this for the rest of us?

Two issues are germane: the first is predicated upon the assumption that network-centric warfare does represent a massive phase change in the conduct of military affairs, if it works as intended. The other is that it may certainly represent a massive investment, but that it makes little or no difference on the ground. In either case, neither the UK nor the European nations within the European security community (which includes but exceeds formal NATO membership) seem able or likely to match the American investment. One implication of this might be, as signalled in an article in the *New York Times* as the air war in Kosovo drew to an end, that the distance between the USA and any other ally was great and increasing and that, in consequence, it might soon become impossible for the USA to go to war alongside anyone else. Such a case would certainly give comfort to those in the USA who neither like nor wish to see their country entangled by alliances, and thereby constrained in its absolute freedom of action around the world. The world's last remaining superpower could, in this view, quite happily be alone in its technological prowess and without risk. Indeed, even with advantage.

Implications for future force structures, command process and modelling

The seminars of 1998 and 1999 from which I have drawn expressed a general caution about too great an enthusiasm for the proposition that the fog of war was dissipated by the arrival of new technologies. Indeed, as observed in the discussion on questions 1 and 2 above, the danger of a single-point failure could be high and the vulnerability of key nodes could be great. In addition, one should perhaps consider another and more fundamental form of failure, which could attach to such a commitment by the USA. In Vietnam, there was a powerful working assumption that technological superiority would, in the end, prevail. Accordingly, metrics, in the form of body-bag counts and the like, were employed, which were supposed to indicate whether or not victory was approaching. Manifestly, neither the technologies nor the metrics did anything other than blind the American public and its military to the reality of the situation, which eventually led to defeat in practice on the ground. Equally, the enthusiastic use of unmanned air weapons during 1998–99 seemed to demonstrate the same strong confidence in technological prowess, as was, more recently, evinced in the concept and conduct of the air campaign against the Serbs in Kosovo. Yet in neither of these later cases was prowess in technology rewarded with devastating and uncontroversial victory, rather the reverse. In the case of the air attacks on Kosovo, it has already become clear that the number of enemy military weapons on the ground actually destroyed was far smaller than the belief or expectation while the war was being conducted. Therefore, one answer to the proposition that the USA would invest heavily in techniques permitting these new forms of remote warfare and network-centric warfare is that they do not produce 'shock and awe' in the eye of potential enemies. They are, it could be argued, 'mirroring' commitments: there is no other enemy on the planet, other than the USA itself, capable of engaging in combat with a country so equipped in these terms.

These important and fundamental attributes of our problem domain clearly put the whole process of C2, including its representation in models, at the centre of the debate.

From the UK's point of view, the prospect of being locked out of close technological and full collaboration with the USA would be regarded as severely detrimental. Therefore, there is a key decision point approaching: it must be decided whether to place investment in ways that will enable the UK to enter engagement with some, if not all, areas of the network-centric vision, or in ways that will enable the UK to cope with the consequences of *not* being part of that vision and practice. The political implication of the latter is, of course, closely linked to the rapidly moving process that has seen an even stronger political commitment to the creation of a European security and defence identity (expressed initially in the St Malo agreement between the British and French governments).

Within this political and military context, Major-General Irwin [4] gave a vision of what a possible set of future force structures might look like:

> We need first to look at what sort of forces will be used for prosecuting war. At the epicentre will be modern forces equipped with the latest high technology fighting and communications systems. Foremost amongst these (we might term them *information age plus forces*) the USA will set a standard in the exploitation of technology which others, including the United Kingdom, will aspire to but are unlikely, for reasons of cost, fully to match. Surrounding this advanced epicentre will be a mass of forces whose organisations and equipment owe more to the past than to the future. Such forces, which we might term *post-industrial age forces*, will belong mostly but not exclusively to the nations of the developing world. These will often arm themselves with second-hand fighting systems no longer required by more advanced armies. They are likely to be larger than information age plus armies, if qualitatively inferior. Enveloping all these will be those groups whose war fighting will be characterised by terrorism, insurgency and subversion. For convenience I shall call these groups *minimalist*.

It seems certain that examples of all three types of armed force will be found around the world for the foreseeable future but not, as I have already hinted, forever. If this is the case, and if circumstances demand that conflict occurs, it seems equally certain that, whichever of the three types of force the protagonists possess, they will be used, simply by virtue of their existence.

In the next chapter, we will look at the nature of command for such information age forces and how we can build models to study the effects of such command processes.

References

1. Moffat, J and Prins, G, 'A revolution in military thinking? – Issues from the 1999 DERA Senior Seminars', *Journal of Defence Science*, Vol. 5, No. 3, pp. 276–9 (July 2000).

2. Alberts, D S, Garstka, J J and Stein, F P, *Network Centric Warfare: Developing and Leveraging Information Superiority*, DoD/CCRP, Washington DC (1999).

3. Toffler, A, *Future Shock*, Bodley Head, London (1970).

4. Irwin, A, 'The challenge for technology in future war', *Journal of Defence Science*, Vol. 5, No. 3, pp. 280–5 (2000).

5. Moffat, J, 'Representing the command and control process in simulation models of conflict', *Journal of the Operational Research Society*, Vol. 51, No. 4, pp. 431–9 (2000).

6. Moffat, J and Catherall, J M, 'Proceedings of the inventiveness workshop on future OA', DERA unpublished report (1998).

7. Prins, G, *Strategy, Force Planning and Diplomatic/Military Operations (DMOs)*, Royal Institute of International Affairs, London (1998).

2
How to represent command in the information age[1]

In Chapter 1, we established the context for our discussion in terms of representing the command process for information age forces, based on a future political and military perspective [1]. It was generally recognised at the start of our research work that this area of research was extremely high risk: indeed it had been the subject of research with NATO nations for many years [2], involving much expenditure but making little progress. The reason for persevering with such work is that issues related to command and control (C2) are becoming central to many questions of interest to decision-makers. Across NATO [3], including the UK, there is a growing realisation that the proper representation of C2 within combat models is very important. Some of these reasons are:

- To show cost-effectiveness of investment in C2 systems: there is a significant number of future C2-related systems, representing a large investment of taxpayers' money, all of which require operational analysis (OA) study in terms of establishing the need for such a system, and for cost-effectiveness trade-off studies.

---

1   This chapter is based on joint research principally with Lorraine Dodd of Qinetiq, and Colin Mason of BAE Systems.

- The UK digitisation of the battlespace, which requires continuing underpinning by OA.
- The need to represent C2 in order to properly represent overall force behaviour and effectiveness. This includes the need to incorporate emerging understanding of the human impact on operational effectiveness.

In addition to the use of current OA models and tools to address immediate requirements, there was thus a need for longer-term research to develop methods of properly representing these effects. In consequence, research was instigated to investigate ways in which the effects of C2 could be incorporated successfully into constructive simulation models of combat – i.e. models that can run in closed form on a computer, and represent the effects of C2, without the need for human intervention during the simulation run.

There are various pressures acting on the OA programme of studies. The first of these is the need to address a wider span of scenarios in studies, reflecting increased uncertainty in the post-Cold War world. Another reflection of this uncertainty is the need to consider a wide range of sensitivity analysis. Finally, there is a continuing requirement to reduce the risk inherent in meeting the timescales of high-level decision-makers by reducing the turnround time for studies. All of these point to the need for constructive simulation models, incorporating the effects of C2, which run at rates very much faster than real time, are easily transportable across scenarios, and capture the essence of information age command. It is the purpose of this chapter to show how such models can be constructed. Although we have chosen the land/air domain as our point of departure (since it is arguably the most difficult case), we have experienced no difficulty in moving the ideas across to the joint, maritime and peacekeeping domains of application.

General approach and research challenges

In a set of technical reports [4–6] an evolution of ideas is described for the representation of C2. This relates to the need, discussed above, for such a representation in fast-running

constructive simulation models of combat, in order to produce a
new generation of such models which are very much faster than
real time, and are easily transportable (i.e. are *agile*). It is the
purpose of our research to develop a set of ideas from which
such agile models can be developed. C2 is taken to represent all
the processes associated with information collection and fusion,
creation of a perception of the situation, and developing a course
of action dependent on that perception.

The evolution of thought that has led to the solution found here
started with my development of aggregate system dynamics
models [7] and my involvement in the early stages of follow-on
development of the model of theatre-level land/air operations
called CLARION, which is now one of Dstl's key models for
analysis.

In addition, this research builds on previous work. The work by
Perry and Moffat [8] indicates that key decisions exist, and that
there is a need to consider at such decision points both external
effects such as force balance and the time available for the
decision, as well as the risk aversion and strategy aims of the
commander. In [9] I discussed the link between key decisions,
concepts of operations and battle outcome. Finally, in [10] Perry
and Moffat indicate the importance of information entropy as a
construct for the effectiveness of sensor systems. All of these
ideas are pulled through into the mission-based approach to C2.
The work was also stimulated by Hughes [11], which indicates
in the overview that new mathematically based techniques for
exploratory simulation modelling represent 'an opportunity to
grow rich crops on this fertile but largely unploughed ground'.

In parallel, work was proceeding, led by Dr Lorraine Dodd, on
the use of cellular automata to model land warfare, emerging
from ideas based on complexity theory (see [4]). Through
further research, these ideas have been brought together and
pushed further in order to produce an improved solution to the
problem of representing C2. This has led, in particular, to what
we now refer to as the *mission-based approach to the
representation of C2*. Ideas emerging from this research, in
particular the concept of interacting Deliberate Planning and
Rapid Planning processes, and the mission-based approach, are
already being incorporated into the next generation of
simulation models of warfare being developed by Dstl.

In the initial stages of the research, two key decisions were taken. The first was that the research ideas should evolve in an evolutionary manner; that the *whole* process should be represented, however crudely, from the start, and that as the research progressed, various parts of the representation would be refined. At each step of the development, and as part of this evolutionary approach, the ideas have been represented in a number of software test beds. These are fast-running models of combat that span a range of different applications. This ensures that the ideas being developed will be applicable to a wide range of model environments. The two key test beds that have been developed are the HiLOCA model (a corps-level model of land combat based on cellular automata) and CLARION+ (a test bed version of the CLARION land/air model mentioned above).

The second key research decision was to put to one side approaches based on sets of decision rules. Past experience indicates that these are not suited to our aims [12].

The approach we have adopted is based on the use of command agents in order to exploit to the full the advantages of the mission-based approach. These represent the various decision-making entities in the model (normally command headquarters at the various levels of the C2 structure). Figure 2.1 shows the structure of one of these command agents. In [5], the C2 process is shown to consist of the interaction of both top-down and bottom-up effects. These are described as *Deliberate Planning* and *Rapid Planning*. Deliberate Planning is appropriate where ample time is available for the consideration of a number of alternative courses of action (CoA) by either 'side' and a CoA can be chosen which is in some sense optimal. Rapid Planning is appropriate where time is short, and expert decision-making under stress leads to a pattern-matching approach. In [5] it is shown that any C2 structure can be described as an interaction between these two processes. We will unfold these thoughts in greater depth later in the chapter.

Architecture

An object-orientated architecture for the implementation of these algorithms in the test beds has been developed, called OACIS. This architecture allows easy creation of new command agents and their interconnection to represent in turn particular

Figure 2.1: Command agent structure

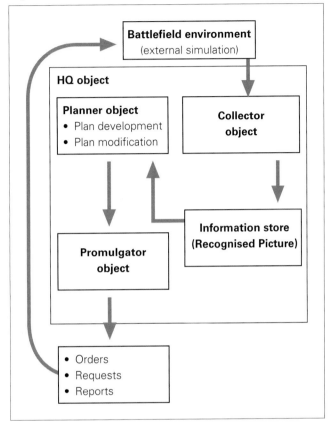

command structures. Two key aspects of this architecture are the representation of the Recognised Picture (RP) as a set of zones of interest to the commander, and the representation of a plan as a Gannt or Pert chart of mission assignments.

Later in this chapter, we discuss the similarity between the OACIS architecture and functionality developed here, and cutting edge ideas of 'layered agents' in artificial intelligence (AI) based on the constructs of cognitive psychology and the interaction between beliefs, desires and intentions (BDI).

Evolution of theoretical ideas

Combat is, by its nature, a complex activity. *Ashby's law of requisite variety*, which is discussed for example in [13] and emerged from the theoretical consideration of general systems as part of cybernetics, indicates that to properly control such a system, the *variety* of the controller (the number of accessible states which it can occupy) must match the variety of the combat system itself. The control system itself, in other words, has to be complex. Some previous attempts at representing C2 in combat models have taken the view that this must inevitably lead to extremely complex models. However, recent developments in complexity theory (see for example [14–16]) indicate another way forward. The essential idea is that a number of interacting units, behaving under small numbers of simple rules or algorithms, can generate extremely complex behaviour, corresponding to an extremely large number of accessible states, or a *high variety configuration*, in cybernetic terms. It follows that, if we choose these simple interactions carefully, the resultant representation of C2 will be sufficient to control, in an acceptable way, the underlying combat model. As part of this careful choice, we need to ensure that the potentially chaotic behaviour generated by the interaction of these simple rules is 'damped' by a top-down C2 structure that remains focused on the overall, high-level, campaign objectives. The fact that very complex emergent behaviour can be produced by a series of simple interactions, based on neighbouring units exhibiting co-operative behaviour (which is of clear relevance to our problem of C2 representation), is shown well in [15].

General structure

It follows from what we have just said that the representation of the C2 process must reflect two different mechanisms. The first is the lower-level interaction of simple rules or algorithms, which generate the required system variety. The second is the need to damp these by a top-down C2 process focused on campaign objectives. Each of these has to be capable of being represented using the same generic HQ/command agent object architecture. We have chosen to do this by following the general psychological structure of Rasmussen's ladder, as a schema for the decision-making process. At the lower levels of command (below about corps, and equivalent in other environments), this will consist of a *stimulus–response* mechanism. In cybernetic terms this is *feedback control*. At the higher level a broader (*cognitive based*) review of the options available to change the current campaign plan (if necessary) will be carried out. In cybernetic terms this is *feedforward control* since it involves the use of a 'model' (i.e. a model within our model) to predict the effects of a particular system change.

This interaction between lower and higher levels is well discussed by van Creveld [17, p. 191] in his consideration of command in mobile, or manoeuvre, warfare:

> Napoleon, it will be remembered, was able to revolutionize war by employing organizational and procedural means in order to overcome and transcend the limits imposed by the technology of the time. This implied, in the first place, the establishment of independent strategic units and a corresponding delegation of authority to the corps commanders; the institution of a – given the state of the technology of the time, none too reliable – two-way information and co-ordination system within the army, to direct which it was necessary to have Berthier's General Staff; and, finally, a directed telescope to check on the operation of that information system and to keep the independence granted to the corps within bounds. Like Napoleon, but in charge of forces whose mobility was far superior and which consequently spread over much larger spaces, the World War II panzer leader was forced to decentralize the chain of command and rely on intelligent initiative at every rank, beginning with the lowest, in order to seize every fleeting opportunity and exploit it to the hilt. Like him, the armoured commander was compelled to institute some means to counterbalance this decentralization and prevent it from degenerating into sheer chaos, which Montgomery for example did by establishing his 'Phantom' system of liaison officers who used car and aircraft to visit every part of the theatre of operations and report back directly to headquarters. Finally, like Napoleon, the armoured commander required a two way communication system to maintain contact with his highly mobile forces – and it was at this point that he was fortunate to have at hand a new technology – radio.

Transition from the OK to the not OK state

Later in the chapter we will discuss the process of Rapid Planning corresponding to the stimulus–response mechanism outlined above. One key aspect of this is the transition between different mission states. This transition potentially occurs when the commander has sensed that his current understanding is no longer congruent with incoming information. To obtain a theoretical understanding of this process we considered catastrophe theory as a possible way of capturing the process involved in higher level decision-making, in particular, the *cusp catastrophe function*. Such a theory-led approach helps to scope the problem and leads the research in fruitful directions. For a description of the cusp catastrophe and its interpretation in terms of two control parameters, the reader is referred to Dockery and Woodcock [18].

C2 of military forces has some analogies with the control systems of the human body – see for example Libicki [19], who says:

> First, the defence of large networks against computer viruses and other illicitly entering material may be helped by understanding how the human immune system defends itself against biological viruses. Second, the ability of the immune system to distinguish between self and non-self (i.e. the pathogenic invader) may have parallels in the application of intelligence-based warfare and low-intensity combat (including counter-terrorism and peace operations). Third, complexity theory is gaining attention as a way of explaining warfare, and the immune system is often invoked as a highly functional complex and adaptive system.

The cusp catastrophe surface in particular describes certain immune responses (see [20]).

It is helpful to consider the way in which the stimulus–response C2 mechanism works in the human brain. A relatively simple example of a human C2 process is hunger control [21]. When the level of blood sugar becomes low, the hypothalamus (in the brain's limbic system) issues orders (via the pituitary gland) to initiate hunger and thence eating behaviour. As blood sugar levels begin to rise, satiation messages are released to cease eating. The hunger–satiation process remains stable while the human is 'unstressed'; however, if there are other physiological stressors (such as puberty) then this process can move into the unstable state of anorexia–bulimia. Then the individual eats only when hunger indicators reach extreme levels, which causes a catastrophic jump into a gorging state. The satiation reaction is then extreme and causes vomiting. The whole C2 cycle has become discontinuous and reactive.

An individual who is subjected to a high degree of prolonged stress (which is usually manifested in the form of multiple, conflicting or uncertain objectives) and who is also being tasked with a physiological trigger to change, can be transported into a region of hypothalamic instability. Neurobiologists refer to three axes: hypothalamus, pituitary and adrenal (the 'HPA axes').

Zeeman (see [22]) applied catastrophe theory to certain facets of human behaviour. The cusp catastrophe model is derived from a quartic potential function (V) whose minima form a surface of stationary points within a three-dimensional manifold, and these can be represented by the three dimensions of a cusp catastrophe manifold. The H and A axes are the control inputs and the P axis measures the output response.

The cusp catastrophe surface is thus a useful way to visualise output response effects of movement through the control surface and it is able to highlight problems of hysteresis. It is compelling to take the cusp catastrophe representation into the military C2 domain by simply re-labelling the HPA axes: the H axis becomes a measure of the combined trigger (perceived threat) indicators, the A axis reflects uncertainty and a number of conflicting objectives, the P axis is the outcome of the trigger process. The extra control parameter reflects the 'stress' and adapts the shape of the response curve. The cusp catastrophe function,

$$\frac{dV}{dx} = x^3 + ax + h = 0$$

supplies the outcome (x) given the stress parameter (a) and the threat parameter (h).

Command stress

General Mordechai Gur, Chief of Staff of the Israeli forces in 1978, is quoted at that time [17] as saying that a proper command system should operate based on three principles:

- a clear definition of the objectives to be attained
- thorough planning
- a proper order of priorities.

It is clear from this that uncertainty of objectives and priorities is the major stressor of the command system. This is captured by considering the two main antagonistic forces in the CoA 'trigger' process to be:

- the cost of changing the CoA (due to conflicts in mission objectives and uncertainties)
- the cost of not changing CoA when the local threat situation demands a change.

It is these two cost measures that give the values for the cusp catastrophe control parameters. The cost of not changing the CoA is directly related to the perceived imminent local threat. The cost of changing CoA is directly related to being at odds with the planned mission and those of adjacent units. Of course, reduction of all the various dynamic variables into two (subjective) measures of cost is far from easy.

The trigger process proposed initially was thus the simple cusp catastrophe cubic function. The first implementation of the approach took as a control parameter (the *normal* factor) the force ratio (as measured by the perceived combat power ratio – PCPR), representing the cost of sustaining the threat situation without a change in mission. The second control parameter (the *splitting* factor) combined perception variance (as measured by Bayesian inference) with a measure of difficulty in changing to the new mission (as measured by the difference in subordinates', neighbours' and higher unit's mission and the desired new mission) to give a measure of the cost of invoking the new mission. The balance between these two costs acted as inputs to the trigger function and the output was a yes/no (i.e. change the mission or stay with the current mission). This approach also requires the previous set of input data as it needs to know from what part of the control (input) space the trigger point is being approached.

Figures 2.2 and 2.3 show our early thoughts on how the situation appraisal process, mission selection and trigger process might interact. Figure 2.2 corresponds to a low value of the splitting factor, and Figure 2.3 to a high value. In Figure 2.2, one pattern of the dynamic linear model (DLM) model of the Bayesian inference process has a much higher probability than the others (see discussion later in the chapter for details of the DLM). This corresponds to low uncertainty in the assessment of enemy strength. The mission of the unit is also in doctrinal accord with those of the superior unit and neighbouring units. Thus the splitting factor of the cusp surface is low, and there is a smooth transition from one mission to another. In Figure 2.3, the high uncertainty in the patterns of force strength leads to a high splitting factor and a resulting relationship which leads to delay and an abrupt transition from one mission to another. The incorporation of a switching model – the cusp catastrophe – provides an elegant opportunity to incorporate aspects of work on information entropy (see [10]). Entropy leads naturally to numerical measures (which may be reduced to just a single number) of the uncertainty in the battlespace picture. These measures, we thought, could be ideal control inputs for the catastrophe model.

The final step in deciding whether or not to change the mission is deciding whether such a change is both feasible and desirable, taking account of all the relevant factors. The following paragraphs discuss the factors that have to be represented (drawn from [4], [23] and [24]).

Inertia

Once a mission has been adopted after a delay, inertia is built in such that it is more difficult to move out of the mission than to move in. This reflects the reluctance of commanders to keep changing their minds.

Hysteresis

Jumping from the 'current mission' to the 'desired mission' occurs at a different point (i.e. a different set of values for the

Figure 2.2: Low splitting factor case

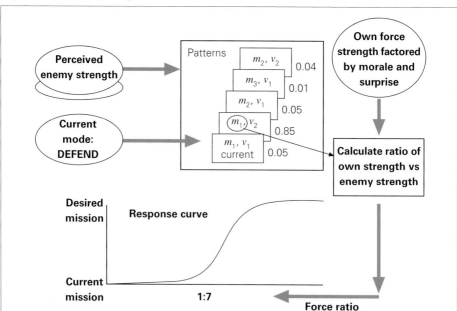

Figure 2.3: High splitting factor case

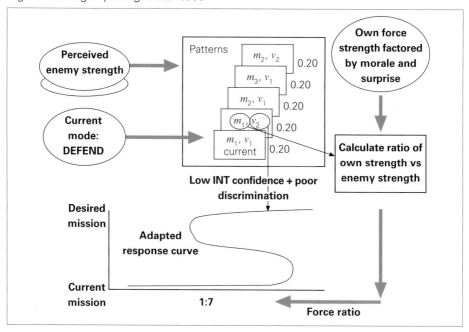

parameters making up the RP from the jump from the 'desired mission' back to the 'current mission').

Stress

The psychological work of Janis and Mann [23], [24] indicates that the two key factors in the decision are the losses incurred due to not changing the mission, and the risks associated with change. The interaction of these two effects leads to four different behaviours:

- *no change* (no conflict – solution possible)
- *change* (no conflict – solution possible)
- *defensive avoidance* (wait for more information)
- *hypervigilance* (conflict – high cost of not changing, and high risk of change – solution to the predicament seems impossible in the time available for the decision).

Another source of stress that has been identified in [4] and the discussion above is 'command stress' caused by uncertainty over objectives and priorities. We thus need to consider the potential conflict between the local commander's desired mission, the mission of his superior commander and the missions of neighbouring units. In summary, to capture the effects of stress, we need to quantify and represent the effect of the following factors:

- the losses incurred due to not changing the mission
- the risks associated with a change of mission
- the conflict between the commander's local desired mission, the mission of the superior commander and the missions of neighbouring units.

In summary, the discussion so far of our approach to Rapid Planning shows that it is *mission-based*, and includes missions as *fuzzy constructs* in the decision process. The key question then is how to represent the effect of these factors. An initial approach is to develop a mathematical algorithm to represent the transition from the OK to the not OK state, taking account of the analogy with the human physiological system and the way in which the factors discussed by Janis and Mann interact with each other.

Review of the general approach

A review of the approach was carried out by a distinguished team from the USA. These were Dr David Alberts, Director of Research, Office of the Assistant Secretary for Defense (C3I), DoD, Dr Richard Hayes, President of Evidence Based Research Inc., Dr Gary Klein of Klein Associates, and Dr Tom Miller, also of Klein Associates. The review was undertaken as a two-day workshop in the UK on 21–22 October 1997. The broad conclusions of the review were very positive, and endorsed the general approach being taken. A number of short-term areas of UK–US information exchange were identified, and possible future collaborative activities were discussed.

A 'return match' was organised under the auspices of Dr David Alberts, Office of the Secretary of Defense, DoD, and took place in Washington DC in March 1999. This led to further UK–US exchange of ideas. The US team made the following key points during the October 1997 meeting [25].

One of the central issues behind the provision of C2 capability is the balancing of centralised and decentralised control – of local autonomy with top-down authority.

It was observed that the C2 organisation requirement depends on the ratio between C2 speed and battle speed: if the battle speed increases above a threshold level, then C2 reverts to local organisation (that is, the system becomes self-organising). Only local commanders can react to sufficiently fast manoeuvre warfare. The *position* of this threshold will depend partly on the speed of response of the entire C2 system (on which the advances inherent in the digital battlefield will have significant impact). The issue is also to be seen in the US Joint Chiefs of Staff (DoD) debate over network-centric versus platform-centric warfare.

Key points made in discussion included the following:

- Commanders have a general sense of 'how things are going' which is captured by the OK/not OK mission states. They take the information that they have and weave it into a plausible story (remark by Klein).
- There will be a need to generate more information (from sensors) when near a boundary or constraint to reduce the

variance of the DLM pattern. Historical analysis might indicate how to move the sensors (e.g. sensors will need to look deeper when in breakthrough mode). When uncertain, some commanders will 'pulse' the system to force the enemy to react.

- Pattern prototypes to capture stimulus–response effects must be defined functionally and not structurally (remark by Klein); in other words, what the pattern means in terms of future function potential for the commander. We must address the rate of change of the means (of the pattern prototypes) with time. Selection of a CoA should be triggered when good boundaries are crossed as well as bad (so that good situations can be exploited as well as bad). We would like to use this approach to model shock and surprise, dithering and paralysis.

- CoA selection must consider the current CoA so that the process is a kind of Markov transition process (actually it is a hidden Markov process that has underlying hidden states which change with time). Can one describe a Markov process that gives the same overall behaviour as the cusp catastrophe surface? (remark by Hayes).

Command arrangements

One of the outcomes of the UK–US workshop was a consideration of the work by Albert and Hayes [26]. Here, a number of differing command arrangements are described that span the major approaches to C2 of armed forces. This categorisation is based on broad-ranging historical research carried out by the US Defense Information Systems Agency into command arrangements including those in the US (in World War II, Korea, Vietnam and various crises), the UK (in World War II and the modern period), the USSR (in World War II and the modern period), Israel (in 1956, 1967 and 1973), China (in the modern period), NATO and others.

These range from command that is almost entirely top-down (e.g. the Chinese Army) to command that is extremely devolved to low level (e.g. the German Army in World War II). These differing structures can be categorised into *order specific*, *objective specific* and *mission specific*, corresponding to increasing devolvement of command responsibility to lower echelons of force [26]:

- order specific – e.g. modern Soviet Army, Chinese Army
- objective specific – e.g. British Army, US Army
- mission specific – e.g. Israeli Army, World War II German Army

In [26], the lowest level corresponds to the class of *mission-oriented command*:

> Each level tends to assign missions to its subordinates and permits them to define further details of the military situation, beginning with the selection of objectives required to successfully complete the mission. The presumption is that the commander on the scene has more current and accurate information than superior headquarters, and has adequate resources to exploit local opportunities and protect the force while accomplishing the mission. Moreover, through a combination of doctrine, training, experience and mission orders, the subordinate commander is presumed to understand the intent and overall concept of operations of the superior commander so that local actions will not be inconsistent with the larger military mission or the actions of other commanders.

The most recent evolution of British Army doctrine [27] has been to move towards this level. A further point is made in [27]; 'the more fluid the circumstances, the lower the decision level should be set'. One aim of our research is to provide an approach that can capture all of these various command arrangements.

The next level up is the *objective-oriented* approach to command arrangements. This assumes (as described in [26])

> some level of trust, creativity and initiative in subordinate commands, but stress synchronisation of assets and actions. As a result, they assume greater co-ordination and more continuous contact between superior and subordinate and among subordinate commands. This provides greater control. These systems were brought to fruition by the resource-rich in attrition wars where superior material and technology

were applied to wear down adversaries with limited resources (such as the Axis powers in World War II).

The final level, the *order-specific* approach, corresponds to very centralised systems where 'historically . . . the commanders at lower levels are considered quite weak and unable or unlikely to take the initiative or develop effective CoA on their own'.

From the above discussion, it is clear that varying command styles or structures can be captured by a combination of both top-down and bottom-up approaches, as shown in Figure 2.4 (based on [26]).

Deliberate and Rapid Planning

Army Doctrine Publication *Command*, the UK doctrine manual for the army [27], relates command function to the level of command, defined as 'high command' at the military strategic and operational levels and 'battle command' at the tactical level. These are similar in concept to the 'initial planning function and broad CoA selection' and 'stimulus–response' levels of decision-making described here. From now on we shall refer to these two command functions as *Deliberate Planning* (relevant to the military strategic and operational level) and *Rapid Planning* (relevant to the tactical level). The amount of time available for planning is also a key determinant in which of these approaches is most relevant. This is normally tied quite tightly to the command hierarchy [28]. As discussed in [5], the combination of these two approaches to planning captures the

Figure 2.4: Possible C2 structures

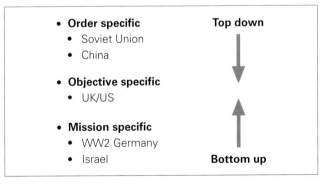

variety of different overall command styles likely to be experienced in practice.

As the operational dynamic becomes more fluid (i.e. the ratio of battle speed to C2 speed increases) the system tends to move towards self-organised local command, as we have discussed. Lack of time at the tactical level due to the increase in this ratio of battle to C2 speed will lead to an increase in more 'intuitive' approaches to decision-making [27]. The use of such approaches (termed 'naturalistic decision-making') has been observed in an analysis of decision-making during high-level UK military war games [29, 30] where 'in general many of the decision approaches employed . . . can be described as naturalistic'. These approaches conform to Klein's recognition primed decision-making (RPDM) model of the decision-making process [31], applicable to expert decision-makers under stress. Discussion with Klein [25] (who is a recognised leader in this field) has confirmed the applicability of this model to our problem.

The essence of the RPDM approach is characterised by the following description [29]:

> In essence, the process begins with the decision-maker considering the situation or problem and trying to recognise familiar aspects of it. If this can be done, he is very likely to retrieve a satisfactory response from his repertoire and will then check this solution by mentally simulating its progress. . . .

It can thus be considered as a form of pattern-matching, where the current perceived situation is compared with a set of mentally stored references (which have been accumulated by experience and training). The best match then gives rise to a potentially feasible CoA. Brander [29] then goes on to say: 'If the situation is not completely familiar, the decision-maker is likely to engage in seeking more information, or in some causal reasoning to account for the perceived aspects of the problem'. Figure 2.5 shows the main steps in the Klein RPDM process, and is drawn from [29].

Figure 2.5: The Klein recognition primed decision-making (RPDM) process

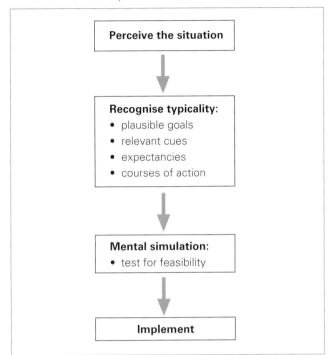

Pattern-matching and the set of alternative missions

In order to capture the essence of the RPDM approach, the Rapid Planning process thus uses a form of pattern-matching, where the patterns are directly linked to possible CoA. This is achieved by further exploiting the mathematical properties of the DLM, which is discussed in more detail later.

In analysing the commander's approach to Rapid Planning, the UK–US review [25] confirmed the need to consider first the idea of OK and non-OK situations. Klein in particular made the point that commanders have a general sense of how things are going, which is captured by the idea of OK/not OK mission states. They take the information they have and weave it into a plausible story (the OK state). At this level, what is required is a method of assessing when the commander is approaching the boundaries of the OK state [25]. While the perception of the pattern of events is such that the commander is in the OK state, he remains in his current mission. When the perception is that the pattern of events has significantly changed, he crosses the boundary of the OK state and has to decide whether to remain with his current mission, or change to a new mission. Corresponding to the spirit of mission command (the lowest of the three levels of C2 structure discussed in Figure 2.4) it is assumed that there is a small set of alternative missions defined in functional terms (such as advance, attack, defend, delay, withdraw). These missions are applicable to any level of command. Thus the Rapid Planning problem is the same at every command level, namely whether to move from one of these missions to another, at any given point in time. This idea of a small set of alternative missions is a key building block in our approach to the representation of command. Putting the problem in this form goes with the grain of agent-based approaches, and ideas developing in computational forms of AI, as we shall see later.

The 'perceived pattern of events' is defined as the recognised picture (RP) in [4] and will in general be defined by a number of attributes. A key notion put forward in [4] is PCPR, i.e. the perceived force ratio in the commander's local area of interest. It is clear that there will be other factors which are also important in war fighting (such as logistics status) and that there may be a totally different set of factors applicable to peace support operations, as discussed in [32]. This approach to Rapid Planning leads to the following steps in the process:

- Quantify the current values of the factors that constitute the RP.
- Determine whether the RP has changed significantly. If not, then the situation is OK, and no mission change is required.
- If the situation is changing significantly, (i.e. we are moving into the not OK situation), compare the pattern corresponding to the RP with a set of fixed patterns which represent the commander's stored understanding.
- Find the best match.
- Test the CoA associated with this pattern for feasibility.
- If feasible, implement mission change.

This forms the basis for the mathematical algorithms that have been developed to implement this approach. We will go into these in full detail later in the chapter.

Neural networks

A final thought on pattern-matching is that this might be done using a neural network. However, it can be shown that for a neural network binary classifier, which minimises the square of the expected error between the predicted class and actual class, the outcome is just the posterior probability. Thus the better the approximation of the neural net assignment, the closer it is to a Bayesian posterior probability.

In addition, the type of Bayesian inference process we have chosen (the DLM approach) corresponds naturally to a number of hypotheses that the commander has about the changing nature of the battlespace, and how this links to a number of fixed patterns in his RP corresponding to the psychological model proposed by Klein.

Overall structure

Figure 2.6 shows the overall structure we have developed, on the basis of the theoretical developments described above, for representing the C2 process, based on the interaction between the Deliberate and Rapid Planning processes.

Intelligence fusion creates the perception that drives the Deliberate Planning process. This normally corresponds to the overall plan created at campaign level. A number of enemy intents (following the BDI philosophy) are represented as possible 'lay-downs' of enemy force, and these intents are updated using Bayesian inference. Each intent thus has a probability associated with it. The Deliberate Planning process uses these intents and associated probabilities, together with a genetic algorithm, to assess the best laydown of friendly forces. Having created this plan, it is then implemented by working out how all the various units get to their objectives. The Deliberate Plan sets the context for the Rapid Planning process. This typically represents short-term reaction to time pressured events at the tactical level, based on local perception. This local perception is created from an unambiguous interpretation of sensor data inputs, as represented by the tactical data fusion process in Figure 2.6. The perception is based on assessing the local situation as defined by a number of key variables. These

Figure 2.6: Overall structure of the C2 process

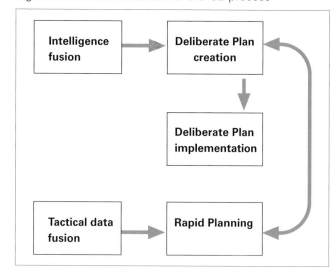

variables of interest map out an RP (or configuration space). Within this RP, particular areas are designated which correspond to associated CoA. By a process of pattern-matching, the perceived local values of variables in the configuration space are compared with these patterns, and a preferred CoA selected. Both the Deliberate and Rapid Planning processes lead to orders to the forces in the battlespace, and there is a process that resolves these.

Agents of AI

Recent research in AI (see for example [33]) has considered the representation and interaction of intelligent agents. This work looks at the problem of modelling agents in a multi-agent environment from the perspective of the designer of an individual agent. In this *agent-centred* view, an agent system is looked upon as consisting of an agent and its environment. The environment is described 'within the agent' by a number of states that are accessible to the agent. The agent updates this representation by perceiving changes in the environment. Actions performed by the agent cause transitions between states. Such agent models are based on the idea of 'deliberative agents'. This representation is based in turn on Simon and Newell's physical symbol system hypothesis [33]; the key assumption is thus that such agents maintain an internal representation of the world, and that there is an explicit mental state that can be modified by some form of symbolic reasoning. Over the past few years, a strong research area in agent design has been the development of deliberative agents using a BDI architecture. We have referred to this structure several times, and it may be helpful here to define these terms more formally.

- *Beliefs* of an agent express its expectations about the current state of the world, and about the likelihood of a CoA achieving certain effects.
- *Desire* specifies preferences for particular world states or CoA – some desires may be incompatible.
- The weak and possibly inconsistent nature of desires lead to the idea of *goals*. These are a consistent subset of desires that the agent might pursue.
- Even if the goals are consistent, however, it is often necessary to select a particular goal (or set of goals) to commit to. It is this process which is called the formation of *intentions*. We use this as a basis for our representation of intent.

The development of increasingly sophisticated BDI-based architectures is described in [33]. This leads in its fullest form to the idea of 'layered agents', as a generic structure for the representation of AI (which can then be applied to products such as mobile robots). These layers correspond to our Deliberate Planning process, where the robot looks ahead (in collaboration with other robots) to avoid collisions and plan its route ahead, a scheduling layer to turn this into a schedule of lower level operations for the individual robot, and our Rapid Planning process (where the robot selects from a small set of alternative possible operations that are functionally defined – e.g. move the left wheel). This lower level we can also consider to be a finite state machine.

It is clear from this that our approach has a certain generic nature, which implies that it is applicable across a range of different applications involving complex C2.

The Rapid Planning process in more detail

The representation of the command agent's Rapid Planning process is influenced by the naturalistic decision-making paradigm, in particular Klein's recognition-primed decision (RPD) model, [31] as we have discussed.

In the RPD model of decision-making the emphasis is not on the generation, and subsequent evaluation, of multiple CoA (as in the rational choice decision-making paradigm of game theory) but rather is on the situation awareness process, i.e. identifying the *situation* that exists in the outside world. Having identified which situation exists the decision-maker then applies *experience* (of previously encountered, similar situations and their associated solutions) to directly, and rapidly, map the 'recognised' situation to an appropriate CoA.

The output of the RPD model is a command decision (the selection of a CoA) made not on the basis of extensive option generation and evaluation but instead by recognising the extant situation and using experience to jump immediately to an appropriate solution (a CoA).

The small set of alternative missions

First, for clarity, we define some terminology:

- The command agent's *mission* is the CoA (an activity) that has been given to the agent by its superior command. In principle, the mission encapsulates the superior commander's intent and sets the goal(s) to be achieved by the subordinate agent.
- The command agent's *posture* is the CoA that the agent is following at any given time.

In this example implementation, both missions and postures have values drawn from the same enumerated set of five CoAs (for land forces), namely:

- CoA 1 = advance
- CoA 2 = attack
- CoA 3 = defend
- CoA 4 = delay
- CoA 5 = withdraw.

This set is *recursive*, i.e. it applies at all levels of command. A command agent is given a mission (a CoA) by its superior. We shall assume that on receipt of a mission (via an order) from its superior a command agent adopts the posture of the same name; this will be referred to as the *ordered posture*. The agent itself cannot change the mission – only the agent's superior can do this. The agent can, however, change its posture.

Implementation via CLARION missions

In the CLARION+ test bed the lowest level of resolution used is the brigade level. At this level the missions assigned to units (command agents) must be translated into actual behaviours that the units are to perform in order to achieve the mission. We define the brigade-level command agent missions/postures in terms of the existing CLARION Close Combat Entity (CCE) missions (Table 2.1). We define the command agent missions and postures in terms of these missions as follows:

- *Advance*: implemented by the mission sequence *Move To* followed by *Secure*, followed by *Defend Static*.
- *Attack*: implemented by the mission sequence *Secure*, followed by *Defend Static*.
- *Defend*: implemented by the *Defend Static* mission.
- *Delay*: implemented by the mission sequence: *Move To*, followed by *Defend Mobile* (the area defended is dependent upon the agent's current mission area).
- *Withdraw:* implemented by the mission sequence *Move To*, followed by *Defend Mobile* (the area defended is dependent upon the agent's current mission area). Note that the *Delay* and *Withdraw* missions/postures are structurally identical but differ in the area that is defended.

Table 2.1: CLARION CCE missions

Mission	Behaviour
Secure	Move directly to the mission area
	Engage any enemy entities that come within weapons range en route
	Engage/intercept enemy entities in the mission area in priority order
Fix	Move directly to the mission area
	Engage any enemy entities that come within weapons range en route
	Engage enemy entities in the mission area in priority order
Defend Static	Move directly to the mission area
	Engage any enemy entities that come within weapons range en route
	Dig in at centre of mission area on arrival. Engage targets in priority order. Do not move
Defend Mobile	Move directly to the mission area
	Engage any enemy entities that come within weapons range en route
	Engage/intercept enemy entities in the mission area in priority order
Move To	Move directly to the centre of the mission area
	Engage enemy entities in contact
Reserve	Move directly to the default position, perform low priority defend task: mission area based on class A sensor range

The Rapid Planning process model

In the RPD model of decision-making the emphasis is on situation awareness (SA). The goal of the SA process is to provide the decision-maker (the command agent) with an understanding of what is happening in the outside world. In particular, the command agent, through SA, tries to answer the question: Is the situation that I perceive in the outside world one that I recognise? Because if I do recognise the situation then my experience (long-term memory) tells me immediately which CoA I should adopt, given this situation.

The focus of the SA process is thus on pattern-matching – analysing the information available about the outside world and trying to match the perceived state of the world to one of an existing array of *patterns* held in the command agent's long-term memory. Each pattern is a representation of a *situation*, and each situation is linked directly to a CoA appropriate to that situation. This linkage of recognisable situation to appropriate CoA, held in the command agent's long-term memory, represents the command agent's *experience* and is what enables the command agent to make decisions rapidly without recourse to extensive option generation and evaluation.

A model of the Rapid Planning process that incorporates the above ideas has been developed and implemented within the CLARION+ test bed. This model runs within a command agent once the command agent has received a mission (via an order) from its superior and has adopted its ordered posture.

The structure of this model is illustrated in Figure 2.7. The model comprises four main stages:

- stage 1: observations analysis and parameter estimation
- stage 2: situation assessment
- stage 3: pattern-matching and preferred posture selection
- stage 4: posture transition.

Stage 1: observations analysis and parameter estimation

Stage 1 of the Rapid Planning process model involves analysing the command agent's current observations of the outside world. The observations are comprised of data received by the command agent via its sensors. The analysis of these data consists of data smoothing and parameter (mean and co-variance) estimation. The data analysis is performed by a collection of DLMs. A DLM is a mathematical structure for modelling and analysing time series processes; see [34].

Such DLM models can take into account several factors making up the RP. However, in the initial version of the Rapid Planning process model described here, for simplicity, decision-making is based upon just one parameter of the battlespace, namely the PCPR (see Stage 3, later). Interviews with commanders, historical analysis of past conflicts and experimental research currently under way confirm this as a dominant parameter in warfighting scenarios, particularly if factored to take account of shock, surprise and other human-related factors. The command agent deduces the PCPR from observations (via sensors) of two quantities in the local area of interest, namely enemy combat power and own force combat power. (The command agent's local area of interest is a circular region centred on the agent. The radius of this region is user-specified, and the agent's RP covers only this region. The RP is thus 'mobile' – it moves with the agent.) The two data input streams are analysed independently within the command agent via a pair of DLM class II mixture models (see [34, §12.3]) – one mixture model tracks the enemy combat power values whilst the other independently tracks own force combat power values. Each class II mixture model comprises four separate DLMs:

- a 'standard' DLM
- an outlier-generating DLM
- a level-change DLM
- a growth-change DLM.

Command hypotheses

Each of these is equivalent to a corresponding hypothesis by the commander about what is happening in his local area of interest: no change; a blip that can be ignored, a step change or a change in slope (growth or decay). These hypotheses relate to the factors that form a vector characterising the RP.

- The 'standard' DLM is a first-order polynomial DLM, representing a system model (M^1) that describes a constant level time series. The parameters estimated by the DLM are the mean and variance of the time series level denoted, at time t, by m_t and C_t respectively.

The other three DLMs in the mixture model are all second-order polynomial DLMs.

- The outlier generating DLM represents a system model (M^2) that describes a transient in the time series.
- The level change DLM represents a system model (M^3) that describes a step change in the time series.

Figure 2.7: The Rapid Planning process model. The symbol ⊗ denotes comparison

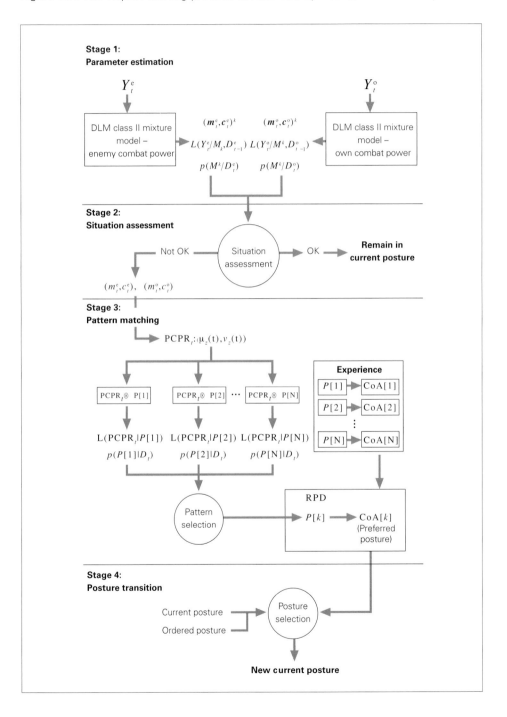

- The growth change DLM represents a system model (M^4) that describes a slope change in the time series.

The parameters estimated by each of these three DLMs are the mean values of the level and the growth rate of the time series (denoted, at time t, by vector $\mathbf{m}_t$) and the associated co-variance of the level and growth rates (denoted, at time t, by matrix $\mathbf{C}_t$).

Recognised picture

The RP is represented by a vector of factors that are considered relevant. For war fighting these will relate to force ratio, logistics status, etc., whereas for peacekeeping they may be dealing with the distribution of refugees, water supplies, and so on. In each case, the DLM formulation updates the assessment of where the commander perceives he is located within the space described by this vector of factors. This corresponds to a multivariate normal distribution as shown in Figure 2.8. The commander's fixed patterns correspond to particular 'areas' (again these are multivariate normal distributions) within this space that he considers important (e.g. high force ratio and good logistics status). To each of these fixed patterns is associated a particular posture (such as *Advance*), representing the direct link between situation assessment and choice of feasible CoA required by the RPDM approach. Figure 2.8 shows these fixed patterns (as bivariate normal distributions in two dimensions), and the current assessment from the DLM (also a bivariate normal distribution). The overlap between the output from the DLM and the fixed patterns is used to update the probability that each of these patterns is the most relevant.

In more detail, and taking as an example enemy and own force strengths as the factors forming the RP, each DLM mixture model operates on an input time series, i.e. a sequence of observations received via sensors from the outside world. For one mixture model the input time series comprises observations of the enemy combat power in the command agent's local area of interest; this time series is denoted by Y^e and it comprises the sequence $Y^e_0, Y^e_1, Y^e_2, ..., Y^e_{t-1}, Y^e_t, Y^e_{t+1}, ...$, where the subscript denotes the time index. For the other mixture model the input time series comprises observations of the own force combat power in the command agent's local area of interest; this time series is denoted by Y^o and it comprises the sequence $Y^o_0, Y^o_1, Y^o_2, ..., Y^o_{t-1}, Y^o_t, Y^o_{t+1}$. Note that the observations in the two

Figure 2.8: Structure of the RP, fixed patterns, and DLM
output

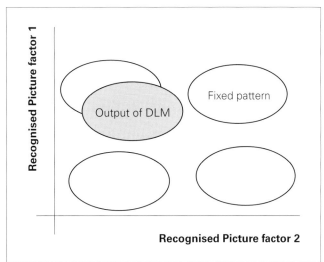

time series need not necessarily occur at the same sequence of
time points – they are independent input streams.

Each DLM mixture model processes its associated time series of
observations in the same way (and independently from the other
DLM mixture model). This is described below for the enemy
combat power time series; an analogous process operates, in
parallel, for the own force combat power time series. Figure 2.7
shows the state of the parameter estimation process after the
observations up to, and including, Y^e_{t-1} have been processed by
the DLM mixture model and before the next observation, Y^e_t is
processed. To process the next enemy combat power
observation, Y^e_t is fed into the DLM mixture model and
analysed. The DLM algorithms follow the Bayesian methods
developed in [34]. At each stage of the process, a probability is
computed for each of the commander's hypotheses
(corresponding to one of the DLM models). These probabilities
are tracked over time to assess whether we are approaching the
boundary of the OK state (i.e. the probability of no change has
declined significantly). The key outputs of the DLM mixture
model are thus:

- Updated estimates of the system model parameters, which
  now take into account the new observation Y^e_t: there are

four sets of these estimates, denoted by $(\mathbf{m}^e_t, \mathbf{C}^e_t)^k$, $k = 1, \ldots, 4$, one produced by each DLM in the mixture model; specifically, the particular values $(\mathbf{m}^e_t, \mathbf{C}^e_t)^j$ are the current estimates of the mean and covariances of the enemy combat power (level and growth) on the assumption that system model M^j represents the time series seen to date.

- The likelihood that the observation Y^e_t would have been obtained from each system model: again, there are four of these (one for each DLM in the mixture model), denoted by $L(Y^e_t \mid M^k, D^e_{t-1})$, $k = 1, \ldots, 4$, where D^e_{t-1} denotes all observations seen up to, but not including, the current observation, Y^e_t.

- The posterior probabilities $p(M^k \mid D^e_t)$, $k = 1, \ldots, 4$, denoting the probability that model M^k is the system model (and commander's hypothesis) that best describes the time series of observations seen to date (D^e_t).

- The posterior probabilities $p(M^k \mid D^e_t)$ (for the enemy combat power observations) and $p(M^k \mid D^o_t)$ (for the own force combat power observations) are updated on a continuous basis as part of the command agent's sensing cycle.

Stage 2: situation assessment

On each C2 cycle (this cycle runs independently of the sensing cycle) the command agent performs a situation assessment to decide if the perceived situation, based on the sensor observations made to date, is currently OK or not OK. The situation assessment is performed in two steps.

The first step of the situation assessment considers the enemy combat power and own force combat power observations separately, as follows. For each DLM mixture model:

- If the 'standard' DLM has the highest posterior probability then the situation is deemed to be OK (because the combat power observed is currently showing a steady level).[2]

---

[2]   In West and Harrison's version of the DLM class II mixture model ([34, §12.3]), the 'standard' model is the linear growth model (the second-order polynomial DLM). It should now be clear why, in our case, we actually need the standard model to be the constant model (the first-order polynomial DLM), representing a system model that describes a constant level time series. It is because a linear growth model used as the standard model (the OK model) might remain the most likely model throughout – so that we would interpret the situation as remaining OK – whilst actually tracking a steady drift of combat power values across a wide range, so that the situation therefore might not always be OK from a PCPR perspective. The only OK situation is the one in which the combat power observations are remaining more or less constant – hence the use of the constant (first-order) DLM.

- If any of the other three DLMs (outlier, level change or growth change models) has the highest posterior probability, then the situation is deemed to be not OK (because the combat power observed has changed from a steady level).

This step generates an OK/not OK result from each DLM mixture model. In the second step, these results are combined, via Table 2.2, to determine an overall assessment of the current situation.

Table 2.2: Situation assessment

	Situation assessment – enemy combat power mixture model	
Situation assessment – own force combat power mixture model	OK	Not OK
OK	OK	Not OK
Not OK	Not OK	Not OK

Thus, the overall situation assessment is OK only if the situation is OK with respect to both the enemy and own force combat power observations. In each of the other cases one or other (and possibly both) of the situation assessments is not OK (there has been a significant change in the enemy and/or own force combat power) and the overall situation assessment is deemed to be not OK.

The idea behind the situation assessment described here is to provide an initial OK/not OK alert to the command agent:

- If the situation is OK the command agent carries on doing whatever it is currently doing – it remains in its current posture; there is no need to do any (Stage 3) pattern-matching and preferred posture selection, because everything is currently OK.
- If the situation is not OK then only in this case does the command agent need to go into Stage 3 of the Rapid Planning process and do some pattern-matching in order to find out if a change in posture is required.

- If the situation is not OK then the command agent invokes Stage 3 of the Rapid Planning process model. Into Stage 3 are passed some key data items,[3] namely $\mathbf{m}^e_t$ and $\mathbf{m}^o_t$ – the current best estimates of the enemy and own force combat power values respectively – and their associated variances, $\mathbf{C}^e_t$ and $\mathbf{C}^o_t$. These 'best' estimates are the values output by the DLM, in each mixture model, which currently has the highest posterior probability.[3]

Stage 3: pattern-matching and preferred posture selection

The purpose of Stage 3 of the Rapid Planning process model is to try to recognise the extant situation in the outside world, based on the data received by the command agent, and to identify the posture (CoA) appropriate to this situation.

The inputs to Stage 3 are $\mathbf{m}^e_t$ and $\mathbf{m}^o_t$ – the current best estimates of the enemy and own force combat power values respectively – and their associated variances, $\mathbf{C}^e_t$ and $\mathbf{C}^o_t$. From these, the PCPR at the current time t, denoted by $PCPR_t$, is calculated. The $PCPR_t$ is a distribution characterised by a mean and variance denoted by $\mu_z(t)$ and $v_z(t)$ respectively in Figure 2.7. The $PCPR_t$ distribution is then fed into the main pattern-matching process.

In the pattern-matching process (see Figures 2.7 and 2.8) we compare the $PCPR_t$ distribution to a number of patterns, denoted by $P[k]$. Each pattern is a representation of one possible situation that could exist in the outside world and the question to be answered is: Which of these patterns (and thence situation) is most likely, given the observed $PCPR_t$?

The comparison (pattern-match) of $PCPR_t$ against a given pattern $P[k]$ yields two outputs:

- $L(PCPR_t \mid P[k])$: the likelihood that $PCPR_t$ would have been obtained had the situation in the outside world been the one represented by pattern $P[k]$.

---

3   In this version of the Rapid Planning process model only the means and variances of the combat power values are used in stage 3. We do not feed forward into stage 3 any of the additional information that is actually available at the end of stage 2, namely: the growth rate and its variance (in the case of second-order polynomial DLMs); and knowledge of which system models are the better descriptors of each combat power time series. Future enhancements to the model will likely make use of this additional information.

- $p(P[k] \mid D_t)$: the posterior probability that pattern $P[k]$ is the one that best represents the situation extant in the outside world, given the time series of (enemy and own force combat power) observations seen to date (D_t).

Having calculated the posterior probability of each pattern $P[1]$, $P[2],\ldots, P[N]$ we select the pattern, $P[k]$, with the highest posterior probability as the one that best represents the situation extant in the outside world. The situation has now been 'recognised' – and it is represented by the selected pattern, $P[k]$.

The next step – and the essence of the RPD model of decision-making – is to invoke the decision-maker's experience and map the recognised situation to an appropriate CoA. Experience is represented (see Figure 2.7) by the set of one-to-one mappings between pattern $P[i]$ and CoA[i], $i = 1, \ldots, N$, stored in the command agent's long-term memory. Thus, the selected pattern $P[k]$, representing the recognised situation, leads directly to the selection of an appropriate CoA, namely CoA[k].

The CoA (CoA[k]) selected in this way is termed the *preferred posture* – it is the posture that the command agent's experience says is most appropriate, given the situation recognised in the agent's local area of interest. The preferred posture is then passed into Stage 4 of the Rapid Planning process model.

Stage 4: posture transition

The output of the (Stage 3) pattern-matching process is a preferred posture (CoA, corresponding to a selection from one of the small set of alternative postures), based on the current, locally determined, PCPR. This posture might be different from the command agent's current posture, which itself might be different from the agent's ordered posture. The purpose of this last stage of the Rapid Planning process model – Stage 4 – is to reconcile the (possible) differences between current, preferred and ordered postures and determine the appropriate posture to be adopted by the command agent, i.e. to model the posture transition process.

One possible option for the posture transition process would be for the command agent simply to adopt the preferred posture automatically without regard to the ordered posture it has been given by its superior commander. Such an agent is driven totally by its perception of its local situation. This would result in a command style that is totally bottom-up. At the other extreme, a totally top-down command style would result if the command agent were simply to always adopt its ordered posture, regardless of the perceived local situation.

However, we can do better than these two extremes. The following describes an intermediate approach that allows the entire spectrum of command styles to be represented – from totally bottom-up to totally top-down. More importantly, it allows the agent to establish a command style that is in between these extremes – a balance between the bottom-up and top-down styles.

As described above, the Rapid Planning process can result in a preferred posture that is different from the agent's ordered posture. We first impose a temporal constraint on how long the agent is allowed to deviate from its ordered posture. This is done via an integer, n, passed to the agent within the order (from the superior command agent) that tasks the agent with its mission. The integer n specifies the number of C2 cycles that the agent is allowed to deviate from the ordered posture. Once n C2 cycles have elapsed since the agent was last in its ordered posture the agent has to return to the ordered posture. The agent is then required to remain in the ordered posture for a number of C2 cycles defined by a second integer, m. Both n and m are user inputs.

Note that if we set n to zero then we have a total top-down command style: subordinate agents cannot deviate from the ordered posture, ever. As n is set to larger and larger values we have a progressively more bottom-up command style. The values n and m can thus be used to 'tune' the C2 organisation and style to what is appropriate for a given scenario.

Bayesian decision algorithms

In Chapter 5, we show how this rather ad-hoc idea can be further refined into an elegant mathematical algorithm by exploiting insights from Bayesian decision-making, and the resultant mathematics of the cusp catastrophe surface. This allows the possibility of representing the psychological states identified by Janis and Mann [24] and discussed earlier in this chapter.

When the not OK situation is detected the agent executes the pattern-matching process using the current PCPR. This results in the set of Bayesian posterior probabilities for the pre-defined patterns (and thence for the associated CoAs – the postures that the agent can adopt). These probabilities define the relative 'preferability' of each pattern, $P[k]$ (and thence the posture associated with each pattern) given the current local situation (defined by the PCPR). Having calculated the posterior pattern probabilities the command agent makes a posture (CoA) transition according to the following algorithm:

Apply temporal constraint:

> IF fewer than m C2 cycles have elapsed since the agent last entered the ordered posture THEN no posture transition is allowed; exit algorithm.
>
> IF n or more C2 cycles have elapsed since the agent was last in the ordered posture THEN change from the current posture to the ordered posture; exit algorithm.
>
> ELSE go to step 2.
>
> Identify the preferred posture: this is the posture associated with the pattern that has the highest posterior probability. Denote this (highest) posterior probability p_{pref}.
>
> IF current posture = preferred posture THEN nothing more to be done; exit algorithm.
>
> ELSE go to step 4.
>
> Get the posterior pattern probability associated with the current posture. Denote this by p_{curr}.
>
> Calculate the differential, ΔP, between the preferred and current pattern probabilities: $\Delta P = p_{pref} - p_{curr}$.
>
> Change from the current posture to the preferred posture, on this C2 cycle, with probability ΔP.

The rationale for using the difference between the preferred and current posture posterior probabilities as the (posture) transition probability is that it should capture a desired effect of making the agent wait longer in its current state (i.e. not making the transition) the more uncertain the situation is. If the preferred pattern stands out well from its surroundings, and there is thus little uncertainty as to what the situation is, then ΔP will be large and a transition to the preferred posture will be favoured on this

C2 cycle. Alternatively, if the preferred pattern does not stand out well from its surroundings, and there is thus uncertainty as to what the situation is, then ΔP will be small and a transition to the preferred posture will not be likely. The overall effect is that the agent makes the posture (CoA) transitions quickly when there is little uncertainty but is more reluctant to change as uncertainty increases.

Mathematical approach to the algorithms

The full mathematical development of these algorithms, for the general case of an RP with several factors, is given in Volume 2 of [35]. A flavour of the approach is given below, which describes the application of the DLM to the case where the RP consists of the PCPR, which is determined by assessing separately the local enemy and own force levels, and their uncertainty, in the commander's local area of interest. This version is currently implemented in the CLARION+ test bed and in a number of 'next generation' simulation models developed by Dstl.

The assessment of local enemy and own force levels and their uncertainty, is represented by using first- and second-order DLMs. These are instances of the general, multivariate normal DLM defined via the quadruple (see [34])

$$\{\mathbf{F}, \mathbf{G}, \mathbf{V}, \mathbf{W}\}_t$$

for each time t, where $\mathbf{F}$ is a known ($n \times$ r) dynamic regression matrix, $\mathbf{G}$ is a known ($n \times n$) state evolution matrix, $\mathbf{V}$ is a known (r $\times$ r) observational variance matrix and $\mathbf{W}$ is a known ($n \times n$) evolution variance matrix. Here, r is the dimension of the observation (column) vector, $\mathbf{Y}$, and n is the dimension of the state vector, θ ($n = 1$ for the first-order DLM and $n = 2$ for the second-order DLM). These defining matrices are constant for all times, t.

The corresponding model equations are:

$$\mathbf{Y}_t = \mathbf{F}_t'\theta_t + v_t, \qquad v_t \sim \mathrm{N}[\mathbf{0}, \mathbf{V}_t],$$

$$\theta_t = \mathbf{G}_t\theta_{t-1} + \omega_t, \qquad \omega_t \sim \mathrm{N}[\mathbf{0}, \mathbf{W}_t],$$

where the error sequences v_t and ω_t are independent and mutually independent and θ_t is the n-dimensional state vector.

The initial information supplied to the DLM is provided by an appropriately sized vector for the initial means ($\mathbf{m}_0$) and matrix for the initial variance ($\mathbf{C}_0$).

Updating equations

The one-step forecast and posterior distributions are given, for each time t, as follows.

- Posterior at $t - 1$:
  $(\theta_{t-1} \mid D_{t-1}) \sim N[\mathbf{m}_{t-1}, \mathbf{C}_{t-1}]$.
- Prior at t:
  $(\theta_t \mid D_{t-1}) \sim N[\mathbf{a}_t, \mathbf{R}_t]$
  where $\mathbf{a}_t = \mathbf{G}_t \mathbf{m}_{t-1}$ and $\mathbf{R}_t = \mathbf{G}_t \mathbf{C}_{t-1} \mathbf{G}_t' + \mathbf{W}_t$.
- One-step forecast:
  $(\mathbf{Y}_t \mid D_{t-1}) \sim N[\mathbf{f}_t, \mathbf{Q}_t]$
  where $\mathbf{f}_t = \mathbf{F}_t' \mathbf{a}_t$ and $\mathbf{Q}_t = \mathbf{F}_t' \mathbf{R}_t \mathbf{F}_t + \mathbf{V}_t$.
- Posterior at t:
  $(\theta_t \mid D_t) \sim N[\mathbf{m}_t, \mathbf{C}_t]$
  with $\mathbf{m}_t = \mathbf{a}_t + \mathbf{A}_t \mathbf{e}_t$ and $\mathbf{C}_t = \mathbf{R}_t - \mathbf{A}_t \mathbf{Q}_t \mathbf{A}_t'$
  where $\mathbf{A}_t = \mathbf{R}_t \mathbf{F}_t \mathbf{Q}_t^{-1}$ and $\mathbf{e}_t = \mathbf{Y}_t - \mathbf{f}_t$.

DLM class II mixture model

The class II mixture model comprises four separate DLMs, defined as follows [34]:

- The *standard DLM* is a first-order polynomial DLM, representing a system model (M^1) that describes a constant level time series. The DLM used here is defined by the quadruple $\{\mathbf{F}, \mathbf{G}, \mathbf{V}, \mathbf{W}\}$, where $\mathbf{F} = 1$, $\mathbf{G} = 1$, $\mathbf{V} = 0.1$, $\mathbf{W} = 0.1$. The initial information used is:

  $\mathbf{m}^e_0 = 0;$ $\mathbf{C}^e_0 = 1;$

  $\mathbf{m}^o_0 = 1;$ $\mathbf{C}^o_0 = 1.$

- The *outlier-generating DLM* is a second-order polynomial DLM, representing a system model (M^2) that describes a transient in the time series. The DLM used here is defined by the quadruple $\{\mathbf{F}, \mathbf{G}, \mathbf{V}, \mathbf{W}\}$, where

$$F = \begin{pmatrix} 1 \\ 0 \end{pmatrix}; \quad G = \begin{pmatrix} 1 & 1 \\ 0 & 1 \end{pmatrix}; \quad V = 25.0; \quad W = \begin{pmatrix} 0.11 & 0.01 \\ 0.01 & 0.01 \end{pmatrix}.$$

The initial information used is:

$$m_0^e = \begin{pmatrix} 0 \\ 0 \end{pmatrix}; \quad C_0^e = \begin{pmatrix} 1 & 0 \\ 0 & 1 \end{pmatrix}; \quad m_0^o = \begin{pmatrix} 1 \\ 0 \end{pmatrix}; \quad C_0^o = \begin{pmatrix} 1 & 0 \\ 0 & 1 \end{pmatrix}.$$

- The *level change DLM* is a second-order polynomial DLM, representing a system model (M^3) that describes a step change in the time series. The DLM used here is defined by the quadruple {**F, G, V, W**} where:

$$F = \begin{pmatrix} 1 \\ 0 \end{pmatrix}; \quad G = \begin{pmatrix} 1 & 1 \\ 0 & 1 \end{pmatrix}; \quad V = 0.1; \quad W = \begin{pmatrix} 10.01 & 0.01 \\ 0.01 & 0.01 \end{pmatrix}.$$

The initial information used is:

$$m_0^e = \begin{pmatrix} 0 \\ 0 \end{pmatrix}; \quad C_0^e = \begin{pmatrix} 1 & 0 \\ 0 & 1 \end{pmatrix}; \quad m_0^o = \begin{pmatrix} 1 \\ 0 \end{pmatrix}; \quad C_0^o = \begin{pmatrix} 1 & 0 \\ 0 & 1 \end{pmatrix}.$$

- The *growth change DLM* is a second-order polynomial DLM, representing a system model (M^4) that describes a slope change in the time series. The DLM used here is defined by the quadruple {**F, G, V, W**} where:

$$F = \begin{pmatrix} 1 \\ 0 \end{pmatrix}; \quad G = \begin{pmatrix} 1 & 1 \\ 0 & 1 \end{pmatrix}; \quad V = 0.1; \quad W = \begin{pmatrix} 1.1 & 1.0 \\ 1.0 & 1.0 \end{pmatrix}.$$

The initial information used is:

$$m_0^e = \begin{pmatrix} 0 \\ 0 \end{pmatrix}; \quad C_0^e = \begin{pmatrix} 1 & 0 \\ 0 & 1 \end{pmatrix}; \quad m_0^o = \begin{pmatrix} 1 \\ 0 \end{pmatrix}; \quad C_0^o = \begin{pmatrix} 1 & 0 \\ 0 & 1 \end{pmatrix}.$$

Bayesian updating

One DLM class II mixture model is used to analyse the observations, Y_t^e, of the enemy combat power in the command agent's local area of interest. A second DLM mixture model is used (independently) to analyse the observations, Y_t^o, of the own force combat power in the command agent's local area of interest.

After processing an observation, a DLM mixture model produces four sets of updated estimates of the system model (M^k) parameters – one from each DLM in the mixture model. These estimates are denoted by $(\mathbf{m}_t^e, \mathbf{C}_t^e)^k$, $k = 1, \ldots, 4$ (for the enemy combat power) and $(\mathbf{m}_t^o, \mathbf{C}_t^o)^k$, $k = 1, \ldots, 4$ (for the own force combat power). The question now is: For each mixture model, which system model (M^1, M^2, M^3 or M^4) best describes the observations seen to date? This is answered via the use of Bayes theorem, as follows.

Consider each DLM mixture model separately. Let the initial prior probability of system model M^k being the 'correct' model be denoted by $p(M^k \mid D_0)$. Such a probability is supplied for each system model ($k = 1, \ldots , 4$) as initial information, and

$$\sum_{k=1}^{4} p(M^k \mid D_0) = 1.$$

Then, at any time t, when the observation Y_t is processed the posterior probability of system model M^k is, by Bayes' theorem,

$$p(M^k \mid D_t) = p(M^k \mid D_{t-1}, Y_t)$$

$$\propto L(Y_t \mid M^k, D_{t-1}) \times p(M^k \mid D_{t-1})$$

i.e.

$$\begin{array}{ccc}
\text{posterior probability} & & \text{likelihood} & & \text{prior probability} \\
\text{of model } k & \propto & \text{of model } k & \times & \text{of model } k
\end{array}$$

The likelihood function, $L(Y_t \mid M^k, D_{t-1})$ is given by

$$L(Y_t \mid M^k, D_{t-1}) \propto \frac{1}{\sqrt{Q_t}} \exp\left[\frac{\frac{1}{2}(Y_t - f_t)}{Q_t} \right]$$

where f_t and Q_t are defined by the forecasting function of the appropriate DLM.

If we wish to 'sensitise' or bias the decision-maker towards one system model rather than another (e.g. to represent a decision-maker's preconceived idea of how the enemy or own force combat power should be behaving) we can introduce the weights, $\pi(k)$, $k = 1, \ldots , 4$, where

$$\sum_{k=1}^{4} \pi(k) = 1.$$

so that

$$p(M^k \mid D_t) \propto L(Y_t \mid M^k, D_{t-1}) \times p(M^k \mid D_{t-1}) \times \pi(k)$$

$$= c \times L(Y_t \mid M^k, D_{t-1}) \times p(M^k \mid D_{t-1}) \times \pi(k)$$

where c is a normalising constant, given by

$$c = 1 \Big/ \left[\sum_{k=1}^{4} \mathrm{L}(Y_t \mid M^k, D_{t-1}) \times p(M^k \mid D_{t-1}) \times \pi(k) \right]$$

to ensure that

$$\sum_{k=1}^{4} p(M^k \mid D_t) = 1.$$

(In Chapter 3 we investigate these weights $\pi(k)$ further, and show how they help to tie together the Deliberate and Rapid Planning processes through the use of Bayesian networks.)

In practice it is necessary to apply a floor to the Bayesian posterior probabilities calculated above.[4] The floor is applied in the following way. The posterior probabilities are first calculated as defined above, normalised so as to sum to unity, i.e.

$$p(M^k \mid D_t) = c \times \mathrm{L}(Y_t \mid M^k, D_{t-1}) \times p(M^k \mid D_{t-1}) \times \pi(k);$$

$$c = 1 \Big/ \left[\sum_{k=1}^{4} \mathrm{L}(Y_t \mid M^k, D_{t-1}) \times p(M^k \mid D_{t-1}) \times \pi(k) \right]$$

We then examine each of the posterior probabilities. If the probability value is greater than, or equal to, the floor value (denoted by f) then we leave it as is; if the probability value is less than the floor value then we set the probability to the floor value:

$$p(M^k \mid D_t) \leftarrow p(M^k \mid D_t); \qquad\qquad p(M^k \mid D_t) \geq f$$

$$p(M^k \mid D_t) \leftarrow f; \qquad\qquad p(M^k \mid D_t) < f$$

Then we re-normalise the posterior probabilities to ensure that

$$\sum_{k=1}^{4} p(M^k \mid D_t) = 1.$$

The value of the floor, f, is user-definable. Currently the default value is $f = 0.02$.

---

4   The purpose of this is to prevent any of the posterior probabilities from becoming too small, as can happen, for example, if one of the system models dominates for a long period of time. If a posterior probability (and thence the prior probability on the next time step) is allowed to decrease unchecked then the ability to discriminate between the system models becomes very sluggish. Even if the likelihood of a system model suddenly becomes very high the product of this with an extremely small prior probability leads to an extremely small posterior probability. In effect the system becomes 'fixated' on one of the models and it becomes difficult (takes a long time) to move over to another model, even if the likelihood of the other model is high. This can be used to represent different command styles.

Command style

Varying the value of the floor level can be used to represent a commander who becomes fixated (a low floor level) in comparison with a commander who keeps his options open (high floor level). A very high floor level will induce dithering and inability to make a decision. The ability to capture such effects was pointed up as being important in early UK–US discussions.

The Deliberate Planning process in more detail

The top-down Deliberate Planning process is based on an analytical decision-making paradigm, often referred to as *rational choice decision-making*. In cybernetic terms it is a feedforward process. This decision-making process complements the naturalistic decision-making (NDM) paradigm upon which the command agent's Rapid Planning process is modelled.

In rational choice decision-making the emphasis is on the explicit generation, and subsequent evaluation, of multiple CoA. A decision criterion is specified and applied to the CoA evaluations to determine the 'best' option, which is then selected as the preferred CoA. This CoA selection is the command decision and is the output of the rational choice decision-making model. As a feedforward process, we expect to have to develop a model of the world, within our agent model environment (i.e. a 'model within a model').

Deliberate Planning – the military perspective

Before considering ways of representing and modelling the Deliberate Planning process we summarise here the planning process from the military perspective – specifically, an army perspective. This summary provides the real-world 'requirement' that our planning model will aspire to satisfy (we say 'aspire' because at this stage in the research we do not expect to take account of all the factors that influence the real-world planning process). Although the army perspective may appear constraining, in practice there has been no problem in transferring these ideas to the joint and maritime domains.

The problems that a military commander and his staff are required to resolve fall into two distinct categories: administrative and operational. Administrative problems are one-sided problems involving situations without an opponent; such problems are not of interest to us at present. We are interested in the operational problems.

Operational problems are two-sided problems that introduce a complicating factor: an opponent. The dynamics of such problems make them difficult to define and harder to resolve, since it is extraordinarily difficult to anticipate another's actions. Furthermore, solutions to such problems are fleeting and the process is dynamically interactive because of the ability of both sides to adjust to the opponent's manoeuvres.

The Deliberate Planning process provides military commanders with the conflict logic to resolve two-sided problems. Although it is not a panacea, a logical process of analysis, such as that provided by the Deliberate Planning process helps commanders to systematise their efforts in resolving a conflict situation. The process has three main phases:

- selection of a CoA and the development of a plan to carry out that CoA
- issuance of directives to carry out the plan
- supervision of the planned action.

Phase 1: CoA selection and planning

War fighting involves the dynamic interactions of opponents. Uncertainties permeate this interactive clash of men and wills. Problems and alternatives abound, yet military commanders must make decisions that decide the actions of these forces. The effective exercise of command depends on the timely solution of such problems. To help them think through their options while applying their experience and talent, commanders employ a decision-making tool – the Formal Estimate.[5] The Formal Estimate is a logical process of reasoning by which a commander considers all the circumstances affecting a military situation and decides the CoA needed to accomplish the assigned mission. In British Army doctrine, the Formal Estimate has four stages:

- stage 1: mission analysis
- stage 2: evaluation of factors
- stage 3: consideration of CoA
- stage 4: the commander's decision.

These stages are described in more detail in the paragraphs below. Note that the estimate process is not to be thought of as a one-off, one-pass activity – as the situation changes, the mission and relevant factors are re-evaluated in a logical manner. The estimate can be looked on as a continuous cycle that can be returned to as and when necessary.

Issued by higher authority, the mission initiates the planning process. *Mission analysis* is the process for extracting and deducing from a superior's orders the tasks – specified and implied – necessary to fulfil the specified mission.

An integral part of each step in the commander's effort to reach a sound decision, the mission is the crucial factor in crafting the estimate. The staff will, first, prioritise multiple missions, if assigned, and list intermediate tasks (assigned or deduced) necessary to accomplish the mission. Next, mission analysis derives the commander's objectives and tasks, yielding a restated mission that governs further efforts. Mission analysis will include:

- a study of the superior's mission and intent, with the formulation of the mission statement
- identification of externally imposed constraints
- identification of objectives

---

5   The Formal Estimate is the process used when there is sufficient time to complete a thorough assessment of the situation [3]. Hence its use here as the basis for the deliberate planning process model. Note that there is a second type of estimate – the Combat Estimate – that is used primarily at the tactical level for decision-making in battles and engagements when time is short. The Combat Estimate process, which is better described by a naturalistic decision-making paradigm than an analytical decision-making paradigm, is the basis for the Rapid Planning process model.

- firm establishment of the relationships between the commander's mission and those of superiors and other commanders
- formulation of a clear statement of the sequencing of multiple tasks.

Once analysis is complete, the resultant restated mission becomes the basis of all command and staff estimates. Using mission analysis, the commander establishes criteria for evaluating the suitability of possible CoA.

The next step in the estimate process is to consider the factors that affect the commander's tasks identified during mission analysis. The following will be included:

Enemy

The purpose here is to evaluate enemy capabilities and intentions (ECIs). ECIs are those CoA of which the enemy is physically capable, and which, if adopted, would materially affect the accomplishment of the assigned mission. The commander must identify potential ECIs and then estimate the likelihood of their adoption by the enemy commander. Generally ECIs fall into broad categories such as Defend, Reinforce, Attack, Withdraw and Delay (DRAW-D). The overarching goal of this process is to produce a list of distinct, mutually exclusive ECIs that describe all of the enemy commander's options. Note that ECIs are not singular actions; rather, they reflect a sequence of actions.

An accurate identification of ECIs requires a commander to think and act from the enemy commander's perspective; yet the commander should not consider ECIs based solely on factual or supposed knowledge of enemy intentions. Without the enemy's mission and objective, the enemy commander's actual CoA is unknown. Even if such information is available, the enemy could change his plans or feign alternate CoA. Therefore, it is essential for the commander to consider all options the enemy is physically capable of carrying out, especially on the tactical level. At the operational level, the commander must rely on assumptions regarding both enemy intentions and capabilities. Above all, the commander and his staff should not dismiss or overlook an ECI because it appears unlikely or unorthodox (herein lies the possibility of the enemy achieving surprise). Finally, the commander ranks retained ECIs from most to least likely, remaining alert for any changes that could alter the ranking.

If time is short or intelligence is limited, only the most likely and most dangerous (worst case) ECIs would probably be examined. The primary source of information on enemy capabilities is the intelligence estimate.

Operational environment

Environmental factors cover topography (terrain, weather) and demography (local population, ethnic, religious and cultural factors).

Friendly forces

The purpose here is to evaluate friendly force capabilities. It will include consideration of:

- the status of own troops (thence the combat power of own troops)
- the status and intentions of friendly flanking, forward and depth formations
- the air and maritime situation (options for ground manoeuvre are bound to be influenced by the prevailing air situation in terms of air superiority and the availability of air support to land operations; the maritime situation will be important in amphibious operations)
- combat service support (CSS).

The assessment of friendly forces is concluded with a comparison of enemy and own strengths, weaknesses and capabilities, termed *relative strengths*. Relative strength is based on force ratios of combat power, modified as necessary by the assessed fighting power of both enemy and own troops. In comparing relative strengths the weaknesses of the enemy, including how his moral and physical cohesion can be attacked, are examined with a view to identifying own force CoAs and the force levels required for particular tasks. Planning yardsticks for movement, and force ratios for particular types of engagement, are employed in the assessment.

Surprise and security

This covers evaluation of opportunities to achieve surprise and measures to limit own troops' vulnerability to hostile activities and threats. It will include consideration of:

- deception of the enemy
- operational security (OPSEC)
- protection of own troops
- command and control warfare (C2W).

Time and space

Both of these factors will constrain the CoA open to the commander. Issues to be considered will include:

- readiness to deploy
- deployment times and movement
- preparation within a theatre of operations.

Other

Other relevant factors to be considered will include:

- rules of engagement (RoE)
- legal constraints and responsibilities
- media relations
- civil–military relations.

At this stage the estimate will have identified a list of tasks necessary to the mission, which are possible and sustainable.

In the next stage of the estimate process the commander and staff formulate potential CoAs for own troops, based on the identified tasks to be undertaken. A CoA should focus on the enemy's centre of gravity or his key vulnerabilities. A CoA reconciles the troops available with the troops required for the identified tasks, includes an outline concept of operations with a clear indication of the main effort, and includes consideration of what the likely enemy reaction to the CoA will be. Each CoA must pass tests for:

- suitability (will it accomplish the mission?)
- feasibility (can it be done?)
- acceptability (is it worth the cost?).

Whether a number of CoAs can be developed and compared depends on the extent to which the options have been narrowed down during the estimate process. For example, at lower tactical levels there may be only one workable CoA and the only decision left to the commander is to allocate combat power to the identified tasks. At higher levels, however, there are more likely to be multiple options for achieving the mission, leading to multiple CoAs that need to be evaluated and compared.

Evaluating and comparing CoAs lies at the heart of the estimate process and involves the analysis of opposing CoA, i.e. evaluation of each ECI's probable effect on the success of each CoA. This analysis yields the predicted outcome for each interaction, including each side's expected losses. The commander is then able to assess the feasibility and acceptability of each CoA during the estimate's next step. The value of the predicted outcomes is that they may highlight the need to consider some action to improve the outcome for one's own forces.

The analysis of opposing CoA consists of four principal steps:

- determining measures of effectiveness (MoE)
- predicting outcomes for each ECI–CoA interaction
- interpreting the results of analysis
- listing viable CoAs, which are retained for further consideration.

The MoE serves as a framework for comparing and testing various CoAs. The MoE must be quantifiable, measurable, and tied to a specific physical objective (identified earlier in the estimate process). It should be recognised that there is a difference among MoEs selected for problems at the tactical, operational and strategic levels of war. There is, moreover, no standard form for expressing outcomes in terms of probability of mission success, rate of advance per day or week, relative rates of attrition, exchange ratios, days of attack, intensity of pressure and so on. The commander's judgement prevails.

When predicting probable outcomes at the operational level, the commander should consider the relative strengths of forces that are likely to engage each other in a theatre of operations. The commander should consider the size and the quality of such forces, their combat readiness and effectiveness, the effect of the physical environment and climate on their actions, and other foreseeable aspects of expected actions. Of the various methods for estimating the relative strengths of tactical-sized forces, especially useful are the results of analyses of previous actual engagements and battles, exercises or war games. Also used are the estimates of the relative strengths of forces arrived at by aggregating and normalising 'firepower' scores.

Having analysed all of the ECI–CoA interactions, the next step is to compare potential CoAs. The commander and the staff list each CoA's advantages and disadvantages, identify actions to overcome disadvantages, make final tests for feasibility and acceptability, and rank the CoAs by relative merit. In weighing the disadvantages of each CoA, the commander and his staff should also attempt to identify additional actions (if any) to minimise or overcome any apparent drawbacks.

To facilitate comparison of the possible CoAs, the staff considers each CoA in terms of a few governing factors selected by the commander. These governing factors are those aspects of the problem that the commander considers to be decisive to the mission's success. Such factors may include terrain, the possibility of surprise, economy of force, usefulness in attaining the next objective, and so forth.

Techniques for comparing CoAs vary, but all must allow the commander to reach a sound decision. A decision matrix can help this process by visually portraying selected indicators. Generally, ECIs are plotted along the horizontal axis of a table, with own force CoAs along the vertical axis. This technique leaves space to compare and rank each CoA versus each ECI. It is an effective method of simplifying an imposing amount of data.

As the final step in the estimate process the commander considers the CoAs open to him to accomplish his mission. He selects his CoA and expresses it as his decision. From the decision he develops his concept of operations that must include his intent. The commander's decision thus has two elements: first, the selection of a CoA, which can be a modification of a proposed CoA; and second, the expression of an outline concept for that action. The decision should therefore state:

- the formation/unit involved (*who?*)
- the commander's intent (*why?*)
- a concept of operations (*what, where and when?*)
- a statement of the main effort.

The commander bases his final decision on the results of mathematical calculations, leavened with a healthy dose of subjective analysis. Calculations alone often will not distinguish clearly among CoAs unless the number and size of forces committed varies significantly. This means the commander must rely heavily on professional judgement and experience to guide decision-making. Before settling on a CoA, the commander applies final litmus tests for feasibility and acceptability, discarding CoAs that fail either test.

In making his decision the commander must remember that a CoA should focus on shattering the enemy's moral and physical cohesion, which can often result from achieving surprise. Where there is a balance to strike between adopting a more predictable or secure approach and selecting a less obvious CoA ultimate success may rest on adopting the CoA least expected by the enemy; this entails calculated risk-taking.

Phase 2: Issuing directives

During the estimate phase of the decision-making process the commander develops a concept of operations for the selected CoA. When communicating the decision, the commander provides the information necessary to begin preparation of the directive. A single source of information encompassing the decisions and tasks essential to execute the assigned mission, the directive formally articulates the decisions reached during the estimate and planning phases.

A good directive is clear, concise, complete and authoritative. The commander clearly outlines each subordinate's missions and tasks, and assigns sufficient forces and assets to allow them to accomplish the required tasks. The directive should provide subordinates with all available information. Finally, it informs them of any changes or modifications to missions, tasks, and allocated forces and assets to meet the shifting requirements of a fluid situation. A directive normally consists of the basic operations order. This will usually contain only that information necessary to convey a clear picture of the general situation, the mission, the CoA, the tasks assigned to subordinate commanders, and any command, control and logistics information of immediate interest to subordinate commanders.

Phase 3: Supervision of the planned action

For many reasons, military actions are rarely executed as envisioned, no matter how carefully and thoroughly planned. Because of their sheer complexity, some aspect of the situation will almost inevitably be overlooked. A subordinate commander, for instance, may have misunderstood the mission assigned by the superior. Some assumptions may turn out to be partially or completely wrong, the opponent may act in some unexpected way, or there may have been mistakes and errors of judgement by the commander or the staff. Leaders must recognise these factors, gauge their effects on the mission and make timely adjustments.

The situation, therefore, needs to be monitored. New information, as it becomes available, is used to re-evaluate the situation and, in turn, the tasks. If the situation changes radically the commander must return to the estimate process, starting at the mission analysis stage, to test whether his mission, decision – or developed plan – are still valid. Supervision of the planned action consists of two steps: planning for supervision before the action begins, and supervision as the action unfolds. Supervision of the planned action provides the necessary feedback that enables the commander to adapt his forces' activities (i.e. re-plan) as the situation evolves.

Modelling the Deliberate Planning process

The above paragraphs describe the Deliberate Planning process from a real-world military perspective. The remaining paragraphs describe the model of this process that has been developed under our research programme.

Operational context

The Deliberate Planning process model must address three main functions:

- develop an initial campaign plan to implement a selected CoA
- issue directives to execute the plan
- supervise the planned action and, if necessary, repair the plan.

A demonstration version of the model runs within a corps-level command agent on each side in the CLARION+ test bed. The operational context of the planning activity is that (on each side) higher authority has given the Corps-level command agent a set of objectives and a mission – either *attack* or *defend* – to be conducted against these objectives (corps-level missions are currently restricted to just attack and defend). In the two-sided conflict, the planner on one side is tasked with attacking each of his objectives whilst the planner on the other side is tasked with defending each of his objectives. (We recognise the possibilities of defend–defend and attack–attack situations, but restrict ourselves at present to the attack–defend situation for simplicity.) Note that the objectives of each planner need not be the same. Each objective lies at the end of an axis. This is illustrated in Figure 2.9 for two sides, Red and Blue.

To achieve its mission, the corps-level command agent has decided to deploy ground forces to his objectives. The ground forces are brigade-sized units, modelled by brigade-level command agents running the Rapid Planning process. A deployment plan is needed: What level of force should be allocated to each objective? It is the Deliberate Planning process model that generates this plan.

When the plan is completed, the corps-level command agent promulgates this, via orders, to the subordinate ground units. (An air allocation element is also included in the plan, but the main focus here is on the ground units.) Each order specifies the particular objective to which the recipient is to deploy. On receipt of their orders the brigade-level command agents deploy to the appropriate objective, as indicated by the arrows in Figure 2.9. Manoeuvre between the axes is expected and frequent as the plan is repaired over time.

Figure 2.9: Deliberate Planning – operational context

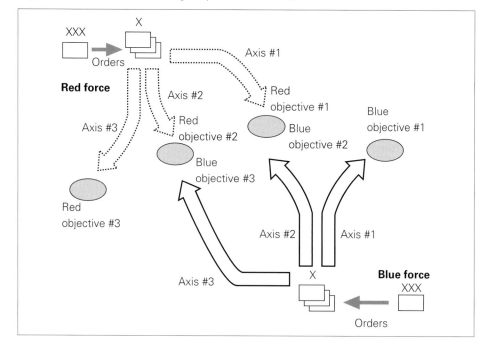

The local behaviour of the brigade-level command agents is governed by their individual decision-making processes. These are modelled using the Rapid Planning process. These agents provide important feedback to the corps-level command agent via situation and status reports. It is this feedback that enables the (Deliberate) planner to carry out supervision and repair of the initial plan, as the situation evolves. These interactions are illustrated in Figure 2.10.

General definitions

Two-sided battle

The battle modelled is two-sided, with one side designated the attacker and one side the defender. Each side has a planner (implemented in a CLARION+ corps-level command agent) responsible for conducting the Deliberate Planning process for the side.

Figure 2.10: Interaction of Deliberate and Rapid Planning
processes

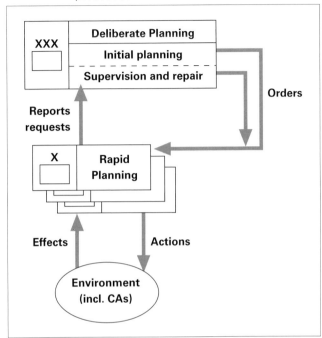

Axes, objectives, avenues of approach, and frontages

- A planner defines a number of *axes* along which he will
  plan to deploy his forces. The number of axes will be small
  – three or four is a reasonable number at this level of
  planning
- At the end of an axis is an *objective*. (We ought to
  recognise the possibility that several different axes could
  end on the same objective, but at this stage we keep things
  simple and assume one unique objective on each axis.) The
  objective is the location the planner wishes his forces to
  reach on the axis. The objectives defined by each side's
  planners need not be the same as each other (see Figure 2.9).
- Each axis also has an *avenue of approach*. This is also a
  route leading to the objective of the axis but this time from
  the perspective of the opposing side – it represents the
  planner's perception of a possible way for the opponent to
  reach the objective on the axis. Again, we ought to
  recognise the possibility that there could be several possible

avenues of approach to a given objective, but again we
keep things simple and assume one unique avenue of
approach to each objective.

In this model the axes and their associated objectives are user-
supplied inputs.

As far as a planner is concerned, his only perception of the
outside world is what is in his RP. Axes, objectives and avenues
of approach therefore must be represented in terms of RP
components. Hence (see Figure 2.11) an axis will be represented
by a set of nodes and links in the RP (shown in bold in Figure
2.11). An axis will start at one RP node and end on another node;
all intermediate nodes and links will be part of the axis. The
node at which an axis ends will be the objective of that axis.
Similarly, the avenue of approach to the axis objective will be
represented by a set of nodes and links in the RP (shown dotted
in Figure 2.11). The avenue of approach will start at one RP
node and end on the axis objective node; all intermediate nodes
and links will be part of the avenue of approach.

The nodes and links constituting an axis (including the
objective) together with the nodes and links constituting the
associated avenue of approach form a higher-level structure that
we call a *channel*.

For the width of axes (the *frontages*) guidance is taken from
standard assumptions: assuming a division-sized formation, an
appropriate defence frontage is 30 km; an appropriate attack
frontage is 15 km. Frontages are needed to support the MoE,
described later.

Only two types of operation are available to the planner – attack
and defend – and a side will do one or the other: the attacker side
will attack on each axis defined by its planner, whilst the
defender side will defend on each axis defined by its planner.

Game theoretic approach

The core of the Deliberate Planning process model is based on
ideas from game theory – the mathematical theory of decision-
making in conflict situations. Game theory was chosen as the
starting point for the Deliberate Planning process model because

Figure 2.11: Axis, objective and avenue of approach

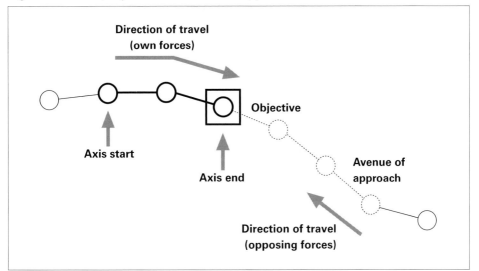

the theory addresses one of the central elements of the Deliberate Planning process, namely the analysis of opposing CoA.

In what follows 'planner' refers to the command agent that is actually doing the Deliberate Planning. The planner is pitted against an opponent – the 'enemy'.

Consider the game pay-off matrix, denoted P, shown in Table 2.3. Here, the rows (columns) represent different CoA available to the planner (enemy). O_i denotes the ith CoA available to the planner and E_i denotes the ith CoA available to the enemy. We define a CoA (CoA) to be a particular (ground and air) force allocation to each objective considered in the planning process.

Table 2.3: Game pay-off matrix P

	E_1	E_2	...	E_S
O_1	P_{11}	P_{12}	...	P_{1S}
O_2	P_{21}	P_{22}	...	P_{2S}
$\vdots$	$\vdots$	$\vdots$	$\vdots$	$\vdots$
O_M	P_{M1}	P_{M2}	...	P_{MS}

It is important to recognise that in this usage of game theory the E_i represent only the planner's *perception* of the CoA that the enemy could follow. Thus, the E_i need not necessarily reflect what the enemy is actually contemplating doing nor necessarily contain the CoA that the enemy will actually take. The quality of the E_i, in terms of how well they predict future states of the conflict, depends on the ability of the planner to judge the enemy's physical capabilities and to divine his intentions.

The interactions of the opposing CoA are represented by the contents of the matrix – the pay-offs, P_{ij}. P_{ij} is the pay-off (more precisely, the *perceived* pay-off, from the planner's perspective) from the enemy to the planner that will occur if the planner takes CoA O_i and the enemy takes CoA E_j. A negative value of P_{ij} denotes a pay-off from the planner to the enemy. By convention, in the game the planner is attempting to maximise the pay-off and the enemy is attempting to minimise it. The pay-off can be thought of as a MoE of the planner playing a particular own CoA against a particular enemy CoA. Each planner – one on the attacking side, one on the defending side – will have a different pay-off matrix, representing each planner's perception of the possible CoAs open to himself (the O_i) and his opponent (the E_j), and the consequences of interactions between them (the P_{ij}).

A game pay-off matrix, of the form shown in Table 2.3, thus encapsulates measures of effectiveness for all possible interactions between opposing (own and enemy) CoA. The essence of the Deliberate Planning model is the analysis, by the planner, of this pay-off matrix (representing the analysis of opposing CoA) and the selection of a single CoA, O_i, that, in some sense, is the 'best' CoA to take, given the perceived enemy capabilities and intentions. The selection of a CoA is the command decision and is a key output of the Deliberate Planning process model.

Analysing the pay-off matrix

The essence of the Deliberate Planning process lies in the analysis of the opposing CoA represented by the game pay-off matrix. The analysis allows the planner to identify the particular CoA, O_i, which yields the 'best' pay-off (the highest MoE), given the perceived CoAs available to the enemy. This O_i is then the CoA that the planner chooses to adopt. The selection of O_i constitutes the command decision.

There are a number of strategies that can be used to analyse the pay-off matrix and select the 'best' CoA. These strategies represent:

- decision-making under certainty
- decision-making under risk
- decision-making under uncertainty.

Which strategy is appropriate, in a given situation, depends upon the degree of knowledge the planner has about the enemy's intentions (the E_i).

The strategy most likely to be relevant in a military planning situation, and the one implemented in the Deliberate Planning model, is the last of these, namely decision-making under uncertainty. Within this strategy there are several different ways of defining the 'best' CoA, depending on the criteria used to measure what is 'best'. Four such criteria (termed decision criteria) that can used are:

- criterion of pessimism (*maximin*)
- criterion of optimism (*maximax*)
- criterion of least regret
- criterion of rationality.

The Deliberate Planning model uses the first and second of these criteria – the criterion of pessimism (also known as the maximin criterion or the Wald criterion), and the criterion of optimism.

As an example, consider the strategy of decision-making under uncertainty combined with a Wald decision criterion, resulting in a pay-off matrix analysis process that represents a conservative decision-making approach in which the planner looks for the (own) CoA that offers the *best guaranteed pay-off*. This is done as follows.

The decision-maker determines the guaranteed pay-offs by asking, for each CoA: What is the worst that can happen if I use this CoA? For a given CoA, O_i, the guaranteed pay-off, denoted by GP_i, is given by

$$GP_i = \min(P_{ij}); \quad j = 1,. \ . \ . \ , S$$

and the planner then selects the O_i for which the corresponding GP_i is greatest. The decision-maker that chooses this CoA can do so knowing the pay-off will be at least

$$\max(GP_i); i = 1,. \ . \ . \ , M$$

no matter what CoA the enemy adopts. The Wald decision criterion minimises the risk involved in making a decision. It is also referred to as the maximin criterion since the minimum pay-off for each of the planner's own CoA is found first and then the CoA chosen is the one which yields the maximum value of these minimum guaranteed pay-offs.

This, then, is the core of the Deliberate Planning process model: establish a planner–enemy CoA interaction (pay-off) matrix and analyse this matrix using the strategy of decision-making under uncertainty with a maximin or maximax decision criterion.

Genetic algorithms

The final step in the process is to develop a plan that takes account of the various enemy intents and their likelihood, and taking account of whether the approach should be maximin or maximax. A plan is defined as a laydown of own forces across the battlespace, and expressed as an allocation to each of the axes of the form shown in Figure 2.9. Clearly, developing such a plan must take account of the intent of the enemy in the way discussed above. This is defined (using the BDI philosophy described earlier) as the perceived laydown of his forces across his perceived set of axes. The creation of the plan is carried out using a genetic algorithm (GA) approach as described below. The GA was chosen in order to allow a certain amount of creativity in the development of such plans. We use here the standard language of GA, as found in [36] for example.

Coding

The information encoded in an individual's bit string is the own force (ground unit and air sortie) allocations to axes.

In the implementation of the GA, the number of bits to use for these parameters will be calculated automatically from the number of own ground units and air sorties available to the planner (which are inputs to the model), as follows.

If the total number of ground units available to the planner is G, the number of bits, b, required for each $n_i(k)$ parameter is the smallest integer for which

$$2^b - 1 \geq G$$

(because, in principle, all of the ground units could be allocated to a single axis). Similarly, for the air sorties: if the total number of air sorties available to the planner, per day, is m_d the number of bits, c, required for each $m_i(k)$ parameter is the smallest integer for which

$$2^c - 1 \geq m_d.$$

Initialisation

We generate a population of individuals and randomly initialise the bits within each individual's string to 1 or 0 with equal probability. The size of the population (the number of individuals) is user-defined; we currently use a population size of 100 individuals.

Evaluation

The fitness of each individual is determined using logistic regression equations derived from historical analysis. These correspond to the 'model within the model' demanded by feedforward control. They allow a particular laydown of force (i.e. own force laydown and a perception of enemy force laydown) to be evaluated in terms of MoE such as rate of advance, likely casualty levels, and probability of breakthrough. These are weighted and added to give an overall fitness measure for a plan. In this version of the GA, we do not test solution fitness against a pre-set threshold. Instead, the GA simply continues for a fixed number of generations. This number is user-input (the default value is 100 generations). The GA then terminates. We then take the best solution as the one encoded by the individual having the highest fitness found to date.[6] In psychological terms, a satisficing rather than optimising approach would lead to early termination rather than later termination of the GA.

Reproduction, cross-over and mutation

The reproduction, cross-over and mutation genetic operators are applied to the population of individuals, as described earlier. The following problem-specific aspects apply:

- The probability of the cross-over operator being applied is user-definable; we currently use a default value of 0.7.
- We use a single cross-over point.
- The probability of the mutation operator being applied is user-definable; we currently use a default value of 0.033.

Implementation

Two-sided GAs representing the creation of both own and enemy plans are encoded in the CLARION+ test bed.

Cautious and bold command

The emergent behaviour of this test bed indicates that the criteron of pessimism (maximin) tends to give rise to attritional types of conflict in which strength is pitted against strength. The criterion of optimism (maximax), on the other hand, tends to give rise to manoeuverist behaviour in which units put their strength against the enemy's weakness, and reinforce success. This appears to be in accord with military expectations in capturing the effects of cautious and bold command.

---

6   During evaluation a copy of the fittest individual found so far (from any generation) is saved. If a subsequent generation produces a fitter individual then this one will replace the previous fittest individual. This means that when the GA does terminate we are not restricted to taking the best solution from the latest generation, but can access the best solution encountered from all generations to date.

Plan implementation and movement

Following the creation of the plan in CLARION+, orders are generated and transmitted to the units. These orders relate to the mission of the unit, the axis to which the unit is allocated, and its objective. The CLARION+ test bed has a very aggregate representation of the movement of units. For other models, however, such as represented by HiLOCA, it is necessary to have a more detailed representation of the routes taken by the forces. Deliberate planning within the HiLOCA test bed is implemented by taking a manually entered description of the routes of the different forces and generating from them a detailed description of the local rules that automata will use to navigate around the battlefield. The routes are defined at a high level with the user only having to select a sequence of objectives for different forces. The plan (called a scenario in HiLOCA) consists of a set of force assignments to routes and is fixed for any given run of the model.

The HiLOCA model computes from the plan a series of going functions and cost functions. These can either be pre-computed offline or dynamically as required while a simulation run is being made. These functions consist of a set of data that specify information about every location on the map. In HiLOCA the map is divided into a regular square grid of nodes, usually at 500 m intervals, and edges connecting to the eight neighbouring nodes (the algorithms can work with a map divided into any arbitrary graph of nodes and edges). The going function specifies for each node the local difficulty of movement on any of the edges incident to that node. The cost function is associated with a going function and an objective. It defines at each node which edge should be used to move by the globally optimal path to reach the associated objective.

Tactical data fusion

This section describes a way of implementing some aspects of tactical data fusion in constructive simulations such as HiLOCA and CLARION+. Currently most simulation models rely on ground truth to supply target identification codes (id-codes);

they thus avoid all the difficulties associated with fusion modelling that immediately present themselves when we take the first step away from perfect identification. For example, the HiLOCA test bed models ISTAR assets and their intelligence reporting explicitly, but only the sensor-to-target detection process is subject to degradation. Once a target has been detected it is immediately tagged with its target id-code taken from the ground truth database. This is being extended to included information fusion effects, as described below.

The Rapid Planning process is driven by algorithms that transform factors in the RP such as PCPR (local to the HQ unit) into one of several operational modes (e.g. attack or defend). Each PCPR is derived from a static analysis of all identified targets, detected and recorded by battlefield sensors, that lie within the area of intelligence interest for the HQ unit. Sensor reports are compiled using the target id-code as the reference field, so that all reports on the same target can be collated and old reports purged. In HiLOCA, timely reports, from different sensors, on the same target add to the confidence value attached to the PCPR. The PCPR and confidence value are then input directly into the decision model. Only when the confidence in the PCPR is greater than a given threshold can the process progress to the selection of an operational mode based on the PCPR.

Fusion over time and state-space

In considering the fusion process at the tactical level for the simulation models of interest, we have come to the conclusion (thus far) that the DLM associated with Rapid Planning is an appropriate modelling technique for time (and state-space) fusion at the level of detail in which we are interested. It offers the desired generality for use across all levels of the C2 functional hierarchy. The DLM-based algorithm has two separate parts:

- a smoothing of the state variables to track levels and consistency
- a pattern-matcher to estimate posterior probabilities of patterns and associated missions.

In current work we are considering the logarithm of the determinant of the DLM covariance matrix as a measure of information entropy, and hence a measure of performance of the data fusion process, as first discussed in [37]. This then forms the basis for representing the scheduling of sensors by a commander over time in order to gain information; sensors are scheduled so as to minimise entropy across the battlespace.

The smoothing process uses estimates of mean-level (signal) variance and state-data variance (noise) to update the mean level of the PCPR and other variables of interest. The current estimate of the mean level can then be matched against pattern templates to indicate the need for a change in CoA. In this way the DLM has fused time-varying state-space data into a change indicator and so has performed both time and state-space fusion. The implementation of a multivariate DLM, including not just PCPR but other important battlespace variables such as logistics status, is thus under active research at the moment.

Target–target confusion

Another key aspect of fusion is target–target confusion. If it is known that two confusable targets are in the same geographical area then the probability of identity should reflect the potential for confusion. Pattern recognition techniques use confusion matrices to register these data across a range of environmental conditions. Such data can be derived from sensor trials, and sensor performance models, or calculated from the cost and going functions described above. This allows us to propagate forward a probability distribution for the position of a unit in the intelligence database. This probability is compared with a new detection to determine if this detection should be fused with an existing detection or not. Confusion measures will need to be supplied from performance models that can track correct responses given a variable sensitivity and a range of false targets.

Initially, if such data is not available from performance models or field trials, it is possible to use the target id-codes. Thus, for each individual detected target (each will have a unique id-code) in the physical domain, the sensor reports associated with that target will contain an array of target-type probabilities and a location (at the time of detection). The reports on the same target are combined by averaging across each sensor's target-type probability arrays (giving sensors equal weight). Different weighting factors can also be used to reflect the identification performance of certain sensors against particular target-types.

The planning assumptions in CLARION+

In developing the assumptions for the representation of Deliberate Planning in CLARION+, it has been possible to abstract a description of the planning process itself which has proved useful to doctrine staff in reflecting on the nature of the planning process.

This process can thus be considered valid from the point of view of military scrutiny. The abstracted version of the process is described below, and assumes that Blue is attacking and Red defending.

The Blue commander's plan identifies a number of objectives. Some of these will be terrain and force related (e.g. occupy an area with at least a certain level of force). Some will be time and force related (e.g. draw down enemy force to level x by time t_x). Others will be a combination of all three (terrain, time and force) and will contain explicit constraints: e.g. occupy an area of ground with at least a certain force level x before time t, while sustaining casualties of less than y.

In essence the plan can be represented as a map of force dispositions over time, and the resultant effects in space and time. It is informed by the information map which is a map of *perceived* enemy and own force dispositions (with associated uncertainties) in space and time. The overall aim is to synchronise battlespace-shaping and manoeuvre elements together in time and space to achieve the objectives. (Shaping of the battlespace means the use of deep operations to obtain favourable conditions in the close battle.)

Having identified his objectives, the Blue joint/land component/corps (as appropriate) commander considers Red options (which will include denial of these Blue objectives).

This will consist firstly of Red's overall intent, the objectives necessary to achieve that intent, and then the course(s) of action necessary to achieve the objectives. This will lead to a Blue perception of Red's avenues of approach to each objective and so to Red's options for deployment of battlespace-shaping assets. At the longest range these are fixed-wing air and naval support, informed by long-range intelligence and sensors. Closer in, assets are fixed-wing, attack helicopters and artillery. Their effect can be defined in terms of a box on the ground that starts to exist at time t_1 and ceases to exist at time t_2. Alternative layouts of these boxes (e.g. across a number of avenues of approach, or parallel to each avenue of approach) will correspond to different plans. The aim of these is to deny Blue objectives (defined in terms of time, force and terrain). Red will also synchronise (in time) deployment of ground manoeuvre units to defend ground objectives.

Blue has to create a plan that takes account of what he thinks Red is going to do (or the set of alternative options for what he thinks Red might do), and create a plan which in spite of these achieves the objectives without breaching the constraints. The missions and time scheduling are then handed out to the units to prosecute the plan.

Blue's plan will thus consist (at joint commander/land component commander/corps level) of, first, an allocation of long-range battlespace-shaping assets to areas that are defined by space and time (e.g. a box covering a certain area that exists only between time t_1 and time t_2). There will also be a time-scheduled deployment of ground manoeuvre assets to axes (avenues of approach to objectives) that is time synchronised to these time/space boxes.

At each command cycle we can check whether time related objectives (e.g. reduction of forces to target levels) or space related (capturing key terrain) objectives have been met – or are on the way to being met – for each side. These will be used to repair the plan (i.e. change allocation of long range assets and manoeuvre forces) to increase the chance of achieving objectives.

Exploitation of this representation of command

The basic set of ideas generated by this research, encapsulated in the phrase *the mission-based approach to C2*, is being pulled through to support the next generation of models being developed by Dstl which support high-level force structure, policy and balance of investment analysis. Some examples are:

- The CLASS model (a corps-level land model which underpins analysis of digitisation of the battlespace (land)), and SIMBAT (a tactical level land model) both employ elements of the Rapid Planning process. SIMBAT in particular is an almost pure instantiation of Rapid Planning, and has been validated by comparison with a number of historical tactical engagements [38].
- WISE, an operational level model of land operations which can also be used in gaming mode, has successfully incorporated the Rapid Planning process, and is currently researching use of an improved version of the Deliberate Planning process algorithms.
- The CLARION model (a key Dstl model of land/air combat at theatre level) will adopt the Rapid Planning process.
- The COMAND model, which will be a key Dstl model of maritime and air forces at theatre level, for use in broad balance of investment and force structure studies, has adopted our approach in its representation of C2, as can be seen from the following quotation from the model specification:

  ### C2 architecture
  COMAND's design has incorporated ideas from work within [our research programme] on the representation of C2 in fast-running simulation models. The research has indicated that combining a top-down approach ('Deliberate Planning') with a bottom-up approach ('Rapid Planning') can capture the likely range of command modes. Rapid Planning represents levels of command where time is short and the commander has to react very promptly to local circumstances, while reconciling this with higher level objectives. Deliberate Planning captures the less time pressured consideration of alternatives, typically carried out at higher levels of

the command structure. Two key elements that have captured these effects in COMAND are thus:

a) a mission-based structure, which is applicable at all levels of the command process. A representation of rapid, time-pressured planning based on moving from one of these missions to another.

b) an ability to create or to evaluate high-level joint plans (based on allocations of force to areas of operation) using aggregate historical-analysis-based measures, and the ability to change these allocations as the model runs, based on how the plan is working out in practice.

Validation

The COMAND model had been validated by comparison with the Falklands War of 1982 ('Operation Corporate'). This, together with the historical validation of the SIMBAT model, means that the C2 representations we have created have been validated at both ends of the model spectrum – from tactical to campaign and theatre level. This gives confidence that the emergent behaviours produced by our representation of such command processes are both credible and valid.

Most recently, Dstl has developed a simulation model of diplomatic/military and other non-warfighting operations called DIAMOND, which directly exploits the OACIS agent architecture developed by our research. DIAMOND has been validated by comparison with historical events in Bosnia (1996), Mozambique (2000) and Sierra Leone (2000).

All of these examples of exploitation of the ideas go with the grain of the Dstl model strategy [39, 40] which placed C2 at the heart of future model developments, and helped to stimulate this research.

References

1. Moffat, J and Prins, G, 'A revolution in military thinking? – Issues from the 1999 DERA Senior Seminars', *Journal of Defence Science*, Vol. 5, No. 3, pp. 276–9 (July 2000).
2. Bjorklund, R C, *The Dollars and Sense of Command and Control*, National Defense University Press, Washington DC (1995).

3. 'Code of best practice on the Assessment of C2', NATO RTO-TR-9, AC/323(SAS)TP/4, (March 1999).

4. Moffat, J, Dodd, L and Catherall, J M, 'Representing the human decision-making process in fast-running constructive simulation models', DERA unpublished report (January 1998).

5. Moffat, J, 'Representing the human decision-making process in fast-running models – Part 2', DERA unpublished report (July 1998).

6. Moffat, J, Dodd, L, et al., 'Representing the human decision-making process in fast-running models – Part 3: Algorithms', DERA unpublished report (March 1999).

7. Moffat, J, 'The system dynamics of future warfare', *European Journal of Operational Research*, Vol. 90, No. 3, pp. 609–18 (1996).

8. Perry, W and Moffat, J, 'Developing models of decision-making', *Journal of the Operational Research Society*, Vol. 48, No. 5, pp. 457–70 (1997).

9. Moffat, J, 'The next generation of UK military satellite communication system', *Journal of the Operational Research Society*, Vol. 49, No. 9, pp. 911–17 (1998).

10. Perry, W and Moffat, J, 'Measuring the effects of knowledge in military campaigns', *Journal of the Operational Research Society*, Vol. 48, No. 10, pp. 965–72 (1997).

11. Hughes, W P (ed.), *Military Modelling for Decision-Making,* 3rd edition, Military Operations Research Society, Alexandra, VA (1997).

12. Sharma, W, 'An overview of C2 representation in IMAGE and GEKNOFLEXE', DERA unpublished report (November 1996).

13. Pidd, M, *Tools for Thinking – Modelling in Management Science,* John Wiley and Sons, Chichester (1996).

14. Allen, P M, 'Dynamic models of evolving systems', *System Dynamics Review*, Vol. 4, No. 1–2, pp. 109–30 (1988).

15. Nowak, M and May, R, 'Evolutionary games and spatial chaos', *Nature*, Vol. 359, No. 6398, pp. 826–9 (October 1992).

16. Alberts, D S and Czerwinski, T J, *Complexity, Global Politics and National Security*, National Defense University Press, Washington DC (1997).

17. van Creveld, M, *Command in War*, Harvard University Press, Cambridge, MA (1985).

18. Dockery, J T and Woodcock, A E R, *The Military Landscape*, Woodhead Publishing, Cambridge, UK (1993).

19. Libicki, M C, 'Defending cyberspace and other metaphors', *Directorate of Advanced Concepts, Technologies and Information Strategies*, Institute for National Strategic Studies, National Defense University, Washington DC (1997).

20. Dodd, L, 'An analogy between the human brain and the military command information system', paper presented at 11th International Symposium on Military Operational Research (ISMOR) 1994).

21. Dodd, L, 'Adaptive C2 for constructive simulations', *Journal of Defence Science*, Vol. 3, No. 1 (1998).

22. Poston, T and Woodcock, A E R, 'Zeeman's catastrophe machine', *Proceedings of the Cambridge Philosophical Society*, Vol. 74, No. 2 (1973).

23. Dodd, L, 'Command decision studies for future conflict', DERA unpublished report (December 1997).

24. Janis, I L and Mann, L, *Decision-making: A Psychological Analysis of Conflict, Choice and Commitment*, Free Press, New York (1977).

25. Moffat, J and Catherall, J, 'US/UK review of TG11 C2 research project', DERA unpublished report (April 1998).

26. Alberts, D and Hayes, R, *Command Arrangements for Peace Operations*, National Defense University Press, Washington DC (May 1995).

27. *Command*, British Army Code No. 71564 (April 1995).

28. Jacques E, *A General Theory of Bureaucracy*, Heinemann, Portsmouth, NH (1976).

29. Brander, G, 'Decision-making behaviour observed during high-level war games', DERA unpublished report (October 1994).

30. Nash, M, 'Approaches to the planning process in OA modelling', Newman and Spurr Report, NSC-336-004, Issue 1.0 (March 1997).

31. Klein, G, 'Recognition primed decisions', *Advances in Man-Machine Systems Research*, Vol. 5, pp. 47–92 (1989).

32. Dodd, L 'Using a dynamic linear model in constructive simulations to provide the link between sensor information and course of action selection', DERA unpublished report (June 1998).

33. Muller, J P, *The Design of Intelligent Agents – A Layered Approach*, Lecture Notes in Artificial Intelligence, Springer-Verlag, Berlin (1996).

34. West, M and Harrison, J, *Bayesian Forecasting and Dynamic Models*, 2nd edition, Springer-Verlag, Berlin (1997).

35. Moffat, J, Dodd, L and Mason, M, 'CRP TG11 Final report on the representation of Command and Control in OA models', Vols 1–4, DERA unpublished report (March 2000).

36. Goldberg, D E, *Genetic Algorithms in Search, Optimisation and Machine Learning*, Addison Wesley, Reading, MA (1989).

37. Noonan, C, 'Measures of effectiveness for data fusion based on information entropy', thesis submitted for PhD, University of Durham (2000).

38. Glover, P, SIMBAT validation with respect to the Rapid Planner. Dstl Unpublished report (October 2001).

39. Wagstaff, K, 'Model strategy', DERA unpublished report (June 1997).

40. Robinson, A, The MOD modelling and simulation strategy for analysis', Dstl unpublished report (October 2000).

3 Resolving the Deliberate and Rapid Planning processes using Bayesian networks

This chapter shows how we can start to weave the Deliberate and Rapid Planning processes together by expressing the complete system as a Bayesian network. Such networks were originally developed as a viable model of the human reasoning process, and thus have clear relevance for our work. This approach has implications (as the chapter shows) for representing the way in which the pattern perceived by the local commander, and hence the mission he chooses, is influenced by his prior disposition of belief, which is in turn influenced by the global awareness of enemy intent. Further weaving together of these two processes is described in Chapters 4 and 5, using Bayesian decision theory. In discussion at the Santa Fe Institute in February 2001, Professor Murray Gell-Mann of the Santa Fe Institute emphasised the need for this weaving process.

Bayesian networks

As described in the previous chapter, the Deliberate Planning process corresponds to the top-down creation of a campaign plan through the consideration of explicit alternative courses of action (CoA); this corresponds to selection of a strategy in a two-sided game where the pay-offs are based on perceptions of the opponent's likely strategies. The Rapid Planning process corresponds to decision-making by experts under stress, and is fundamentally a pattern-matching process. This is described by algorithms using Bayesian inference and dynamic linear models (DLM). One of the main areas requiring further work is the proper interaction of the Deliberate and Rapid Planning processes. We show here that it is possible to represent both these processes as Bayesian networks, and this gives insight into how to stitch them together, thereby improving the algorithms.

One of the best expositions of Bayesian networks is that of Pearl [1, 2]. In [2] he puts forward arguments for this approach as the basis of a viable model of human reasoning. Since we are concerned here with the representation of the command and control (C2) process, which is essentially human reasoning applied to the problems of military command, the potential of Pearl's work is clear.

The network as a graph

This discussion is based on Pearl's work [1, 2]. In particular, the notation developed in [2] is used here. Pearl defines a Bayesian network (also called a 'belief network') as a type of graph. That is, it can be drawn as a set of nodes linked together by arcs. The links have arrows on them indicating the direction of causality (from conditions or hypotheses to consequences). Thus it is what is known as a *directed* graph. No 'cycles' (a set of links forming a circle, with all arrows pointing in the same direction) are allowed, hence no feedback can occur. Thus it is what is known as an *acyclic* graph. The nodes of the graph represent propositions, the arcs represent direct dependency between linked propositions, and the strengths of these dependencies are quantified by conditional probabilities. In this formulation, the probability of a data value is usually normalised out, as in the first example below. All of the examples given display the property of conditional independence. This is discussed at greater length in the third example (of a tree structure).

First example: a single link

Consider first the simplest network consisting of just two nodes X and Y, and a single link $X \rightarrow Y$ where X and Y are propositions yet to be evaluated. Assume now that evidence e that Y takes the value y is observed. How does this affect our belief that X has a given value? The answer is given by Bayesian updating of the belief corresponding to the proposition X. We thus have that the current belief in the value of the proposition X, which we write as $BEL(x)$, is given by

$$BEL(x) = P(x \mid e) = \alpha P(x) \lambda(x)$$

where $\alpha = 1/P(e)$ (a normalising factor), $P(x)$ is the prior probability of x and $\lambda(x)$ is the likelihood, given by

$$\lambda(x) = P(e \mid x) = P(Y = y \mid x) \qquad\qquad (1)$$

We write the last term as follows:

$$P(Y = y \mid x) = M_{y|x}$$

Note that these values $M_{y|x}$ can be pre-stored at the node point Y waiting for the precise observation e of Y to occur. The value $M_{y|x}$ can then be transmitted to the node X allowing the evaluation of $\lambda(x)$ from equation (1) and hence the evaluation of $BEL(x)$. Note that the direction of influence goes from X to Y, while the propagation of inference (evidence and updating) goes from Y to X via the evaluation of λ.

Second example: a chain

As a second example of such a network, consider now a chain of several propositions of the form shown in Figure 3.1, and where updating can occur in either direction.

Here the chain of inference is started and ended by observed data values $e+$ and $e-$, and we want to calculate the weight of belief of the proposition X given these two data values.

Figure 3.1: A chain of propositions

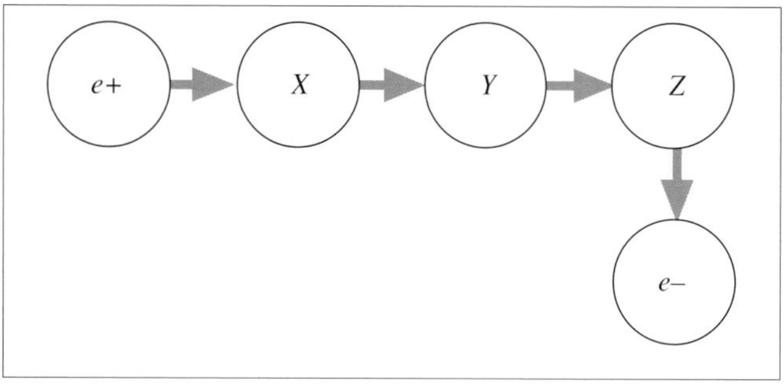

Define the conditional probability of $e-$ given x as

$\lambda(x) = P(e- \mid x)$

and define the conditional probability of x given $e+$ as

$\pi(x) = P(x \mid e+)$

We then have that

$BEL(x) = P(x \mid e+, e-)$

$= \alpha P(e- \mid x, e+)P(x \mid e+)$

$= \alpha P(e- \mid x)P(x \mid e+)$

$= \alpha \lambda(x)\pi(x)$

From our first example with just one link, we can see that $\lambda(x)$ will propagate in the direction opposite to the arrows of influence in Figure 3.1. By symmetry we would expect $\pi(x)$ to propagate in the same direction as the arrows of influence. That this is the case is shown by the recurrence relations which are now derived:

$\pi(y) = P(y \mid e+)$

$= \sum_x P(y \mid x, e+)P(x \mid e+)$

$= \sum_x P(y \mid x)P(x \mid e+)$

$= \pi(x) . M_{y \mid x}$

The dot in between the two terms in the last line above means that the product expression should be summed over the repeated variable – that is the x value, using Pearl's notation [2].

The effect of the data value $e+$ on the weight of belief of the various propositions (X, Y, Z) in the chain can thus be calculated by repeated application of this recursive expression. As can be seen, it moves from the left-hand end of the chain to the right, following the arrows of influence in Figure 3.1.

In a similar way, we calculate the effect of the data value $e-$:

$$\lambda(x) = P(e- \mid x)$$
$$= \sum_{y} P(e- \mid y, x) P(y \mid x)$$
$$= \sum_{y} P(e- \mid y) P(y \mid x)$$
$$= \lambda(y) . M_{y|x}$$

We thus have a recursive relationship that moves in the opposite direction to the arrows of influence in Figure 3.1, as we expected. At any time, as we have shown, the total belief in proposition '$X = x$' is:

$$BEL(x) = \alpha \, \lambda(x)\pi(x)$$

Third example: a simple tree structure

The simple tree of influence is shown at Figure 3.2 (using Pearl's notation). The tree is rooted at the proposition U, and influence propagates through X to nodes Y and Z. In an extended network, Proposition U represents the effect of the rest of the network on X, except for the tree rooted at X. This follows from the assumption of *conditional independence*. This means that all the influence of the network on a proposition such as X is reflected in the local influence between X and its nearest neighbours in the network. Following on this thought, the tree 'below' X is represented in Figure 3.2 by the propositions Y and Z, but in general these propositions could lead to a more extended tree network rooted at X. For structures like that shown at Figure 3.2, the higher levels such as U typically correspond to higher-level propositions, and the lower nodes such as Y and Z correspond to lower-level propositions or data values. We assume that evidence e_y- is available at the node Y and evidence e_z- is available at the node Z. There is also evidence e_{x+} available from the rest of the network, which influences the proposition U in the same way that it influences X in Figure 3.1. We can fuse

Figure 3.2: A simple tree of propositions

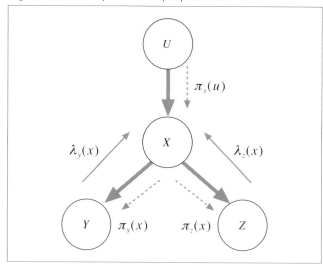

these various (independent) pieces of data together and update our belief in X in the following way.

Firstly, using Pearl's notation again [2], the total evidence available at X from Y and Z (i.e. the total evidence available from the tree rooted at X) is defined as

$$e_x- = e_y- \cup e_z-$$

We then have that

$$\lambda(x) = P(e_x- \mid x)$$

$$= P(e_y-, e_z- \mid x)$$

$$= P(e_y- \mid x) P(e_z- \mid x)$$

$$= \lambda_y(x)\lambda_z(x)$$

and that

$$\pi(x) = P(x \mid e_x+)$$

$$= \sum_u P(x \mid e_x+, u)P(u \mid e_x+)$$

$$= \sum_u P(x \mid u)\pi_x(u)$$

$$= M_{x|u} \cdot \pi_x(u)$$

where $\pi_x(u)$ is defined as $P(u \mid e_x+)$, and we have exploited the conditional independence relation between x and u. The sum in the above derivation is over the different possible values u of the Proposition U.

Hence we can express the current belief in x, $BEL(x)$, as:

$$BEL(x) = P(x \mid e_x+, e_x-)$$

$$= \alpha P(e_x- \mid e_x+, x)P(x \mid e_x+)$$

$$= \alpha P(e_x- \mid x)P(x \mid e_x+)$$

$$= \alpha \lambda(x)\pi(x)$$

$$= \alpha \lambda_y(x)\lambda_z(x)\pi_x(u) \cdot M_{x/u}$$

We can consider this to be the *fused* total strength of belief due to information derived from the upper and lower parts of the network. Paraphrasing Pearl [2], it fuses together the top-down 'causal or predictive' support derived from the rest of the network, with the 'diagnostic or retrospective' support derived from the tree rooted at X.

The dynamic linear model as part of a Bayesian network

The dynamic linear model (DLM) plays a central part in the construction of algorithms for Intelligence fusion as part of the Deliberate Planning process. As discussed in Chapter 2, it is also central to assessing the value of the factors that constitute the recognised picture (RP) used as part of the Rapid Planning process. If we can express such DLMs as Bayesian networks, this would form the core of a description of the sensing and situation assessment process as a complete such network. This should then lead to insights into how to extend the present state of understanding and analysis. We are dealing here with a mechanism that essentially converts a dynamically varying process of observations into assumptions about the likelihood of a number of discrete states.

It is possible to derive the DLM from first principles, in a way which shows that, at heart, it is a conditional distribution process. As described in [3], the general multivariate DLM consists of two equations. The first of these, known as the *observation equation*, relates the observation vector y_t at time t to the state of the system at time t as described by the system vector θ_t through the relation:

$$y_t = F_t \theta_t + v_t$$

where v_t is a noise vector drawn at random from the multivariate normal distribution N(0, V_t), and F_t is a matrix of known independent variables or constants.

The evolution of the system over time is described by the *system equation*. This relates the value of the state vector θ_t at time t to the value at the previous time-step $t - 1$. The relationship is assumed to be of the form

$$\theta_t = G_t \theta_{t-1} + w_t$$

where G_t is a matrix of known constants or variables and w_t is a noise vector drawn at random from a multivariate normal distribution N(0, W_t).

Fundamentally, we are attempting to assess how the system is evolving in time, as it takes account of the data values y. Thus we want to assess the system state vector θ_t at time t, given its value at time $t - 1$ and the data y_t.

By recursive use of the system equation, it is clear that for any time t the distribution of θ_t (given the information available at time t) is multivariate normal, provided that the initial assumed distribution of θ_0 is multivariate normal. The information available at time $t - 1$ is D_{t-1}. Define the conditional distribution of θ_{t-1} given D_{t-1} as a multivariate normal distribution with mean M_{t-1} and covariance matrix C_{t-1}. Similarly, define the mean and covariance matrix of θ_t by M_t and C_t respectively. These represent best estimates given the information available at time t. The question to be answered is: what is the relation between these two distributions at $t - 1$ and t?

Symbolically we can write this in terms of conditional distributions as:

$$(\theta_{t-1} \mid D_{t-1}) \approx N(M_{t-1}, C_{t-1})$$

and

$$(\theta_t \mid D_t) \approx N(M_t, C_t)$$

We consider first the joint distribution of the vector

$$\begin{pmatrix} \theta_t \\ y_t \end{pmatrix}$$

as assessed with the information available at time $t - 1$. This can be considered as the combination of the two distributions $(\theta_t \mid D_{t-1})$ and $(y_t \mid D_{t-1})$ as shown in Figure 3.3.

From the system equation, denoting the expectation of a variable by E, we have

$$E(\theta_t) = GE(\theta_{t-1}) + E(w_t) = GM_{t-1}$$

and from the observation equation we have

$$E(y_t) = F_t E(\theta_t) + E(v_t) = F_t GM_{t-1} = \hat{y}_t$$

which is the one-step-ahead forecast of y_t.

Given the actual value of the vector of observations y, the picture above changes to the one in Figure 3.4. We can see from this that the DLM can indeed be regarded as a conditional distribution.

Figure 3.3: Joint distribution of the system state (θ) and data (y)

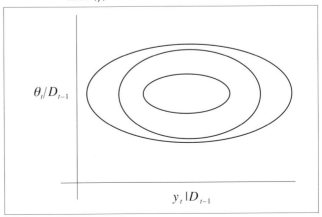

Figure 3.4: Updated distribution of the system state (θ)

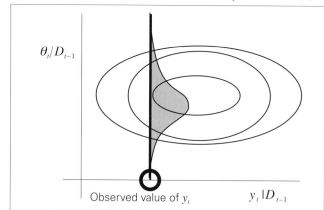

The point of deriving these relationships from first principles is that it clearly and transparently indicates that the updated estimate of the system state, given by the distribution of ($\theta_t \mid y_t$) is indeed a *conditional* distribution corresponding to a slice through the joint distribution as shown in Figure 3.4. The position of this slice is determined by the collapse of the forecast of the data vector y to its actual value y_t at time t.

The Deliberate Planning process

This process is described in detail in Chapter 2. For clarity, we concentrate on the key stages in the process, which are assessments of:

- the situation at each of the named areas of interest on each of the axes under consideration; we shall refer to these as *nodes* here for convenience
- the intent of the enemy, by which we mean his likely distribution of force across the axes, given our observations at each of the nodes.

The first of these stages uses the DLM to update the system state (the expected level of enemy force at the node), given the data, and we can represent this as a conditional probability in the way described in the previous chapter.

The second stage uses Bayesian inference to calculate the posterior probability of each enemy intent (where an intent corresponds to an allocation of force to each of the axes).

Figure 3.5 shows the complete process of inference in diagrammatic terms. A Bayesian network representation of this process, linking hypotheses to consequences, is shown in Figure 3.6.

Figure 3.5: Deliberate Planning inference

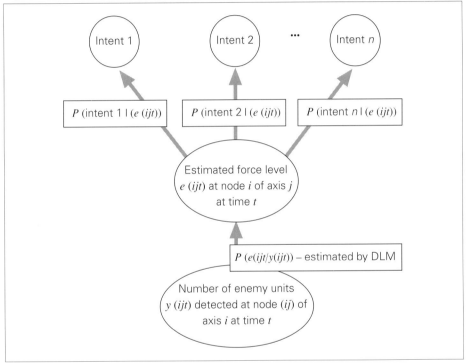

Figure 3.6: Deliberate Planning Bayesian network

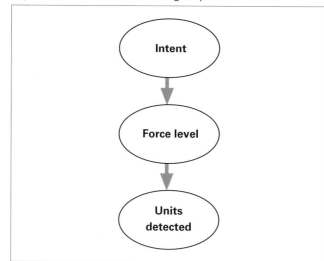

The Rapid Planning process

The Rapid Planning Process is also described in detail in Chapter 2. Again, for clarity we concentrate on the essentials of the process. The key stages in this case are:

- assessing whether the situation has changed, by considering the likelihood of each of the four DLM models in a type II DLM mixture model
- if the situation has changed significantly, determining by Bayesian inference, the probabilities to be associated with the pre-stored patterns $P(1) \ldots P(k)$. These patterns are multivariate normal distributions corresponding to the factors of the RP.

The inference process is again shown in Figure 3.7, and a Bayesian network representation (at an aggregate level) of this process is shown in Figure 3.8.

Figure 3.7: Rapid Planning inference

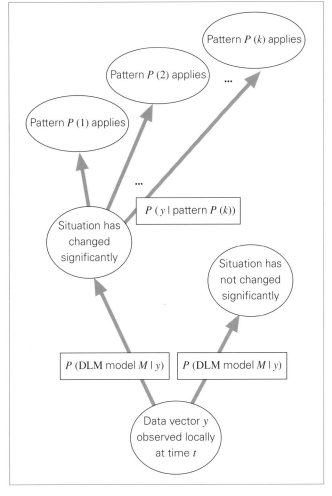

Linkage between Deliberate and Rapid Planning

By comparing Figures 3.6–3.8, it is clear from the Bayesian network representation that the link between the Deliberate and Rapid Planning processes is made through the relationship between belief in perceived enemy intent and belief in a particular pattern by the local commander. The belief in enemy intent (leading to a probability associated with each intent), is itself a direct consequence of the perceived disposition of enemy force as assessed by own sensors, and is described under the

Figure 3.8: Rapid Planning Bayesian network

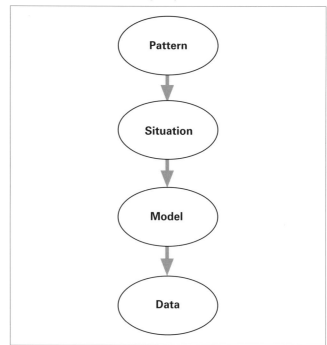

heading of 'intelligence fusion'. If this information is passed to the local commander and used to update his local picture, this will influence the values assessed by the local commander for the factors that constitute his local picture. For example, if it increases the local perception of force ratio, this will influence the choice of pattern and hence choice of posture. We can represent this passage of information through the conditional probability

P(pattern k for local commander| intent j)

Thus information at the higher level influences the local commander's prior belief in his local situation, which is then moderated by local data to produce a local posterior belief. This then captures the way information is passed between the top-down intelligence fusion part of Deliberate Planning, and the local picture available to the local commander. It will vary for different local commanders in general since the information passed to the local picture will be different.

Figure 3.9: Bayesian network tree for pattern belief

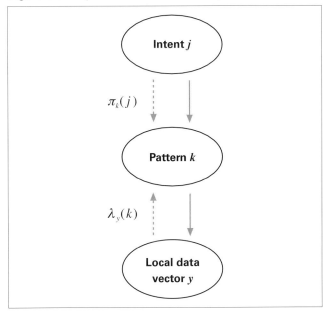

Fusion of belief

If we now consider again the Bayesian network figures, can this approach give us further guidance in how to fuse this top-down intelligence coherently with information gathered at local level in order to give an overall assessment of belief for each pattern available to the local commander? Figure 3.9 shows a Bayesian network tree formulation of our problem.

The evidence available is defined here as:

$$e_y{-} = y = e_k{-}$$

$$e_k{+} = e$$

where y is the local data vector perceived by the local commander, and e is the overall perceived enemy force disposition.

For the derivation below, we let k be the pattern under consideration at the local level, and j represents one of the overall enemy intents being considered at the intelligence fusion level of input into the Deliberate Planning process, in conjunction with the perceived overall disposition e of enemy force.

In Pearl's notation we then have:

$$\lambda(k) = \lambda_y(k) = P(e_k- \mid k) = P(y \mid k)$$

$$\pi_k(j) = P(j \mid e_k+)$$

$$BEL(k) = P(k \mid e_k+, e_k-)$$

$$= \lambda P(e_k- \mid e_k+, k)P(k \mid e_k+)$$

$$= \alpha P(e_k- \mid k)P(k \mid e_k+)$$

$$= \alpha \lambda(k)\pi(k)$$

where

$$\lambda(k) = P(e_k- \mid k) = \lambda_y(k)$$

and

$$\pi(k) = P(k \mid e_k+)$$
$$= \sum P(k \mid j)P(j \mid e_k+)$$
$$= \sum P(k \mid j)\pi_k(j)$$
$$= M_{k|j} \cdot \pi_k(j)$$

Thus

$$BEL(k) = \alpha \lambda_y(k)\pi_k(j) \cdot M_{k|j} \qquad\qquad (2)$$

where $BEL(k)$ represents the total fused belief in pattern k by the local commander, taking account of both information available from the overall intelligence and perception process, and his own local sensors.

Compare this now with the Bayesian expression (from Chapter 2) used to derive the probability of pattern $[k]$:

$$p(P[k] \mid D_t) = cL(PCPR_t \mid P[k], D_{t-1})p(P[k] \mid D_{t-1})\pi(k) \qquad (3)$$

The first term is a normalising constant. The second is the likelihood of the new data given pattern $[k]$, the third term is the prior probability of pattern [k], and the fourth term is a weighting factor conditioning the commander's general expectation as to which patterns are likely to arise.

We can interpret these in Bayesian network terms as follows, to allow a comparison with what we have derived above at equation (2):

- $p(P[k] \mid D_t)$ is the belief in pattern k given all available information $= BEL(k)$
- c is a normalising constant $= \alpha$
- $L(\text{PCPR}_t \mid P[k], D_{t-1})$ is the probability of local data given pattern $k = \lambda_y(k)$

It thus follows by comparing equations (2) and (3) that the expression $p(P[k] \mid D_{t-1})\pi(k)$ from equation (3) is expressible as the terms $\pi_k(j)$. $M_{k/j}$ of equation (2). Expressed in words, this latter expression is the sum, over intents j, of probability (pattern k | intent j) × probability (intent j | evidence e_k+ concerning the perceived overall disposition of enemy force).

This thus allows the weight $\pi(k)$ in equation (3) to dynamically modify the prior disposition of belief of the local commander, in terms of the information available from the top-down perception of overall enemy disposition.

In summary, we have shown that the Deliberate and Rapid Planning processes, which lie at the basis of the mission-based approach to C2, can be described as Bayesian networks. Moreover, consideration of how they link together as a Bayesian tree structure gives guidance as to how to link together information available at the Deliberate Planning level and information available to the local commander. This process allows the local commander's prior perception to be informed by information available from the top-down perception of overall enemy disposition and leads to improvement in the algorithmic representation of the command process. The implication of this process is that at local level, neighbouring units will tend to adopt more similar missions (i.e. will self-synchronise).

References

1. Pearl. J, 'Fusion, propagation and structuring in belief networks', *Artificial Intelligence*, Vol. 29, No. 3, pp. 241–88 (1986).

2. Pearl, J, *Probabilistic Inference in Intelligent Systems*, Morgan Kaufmann, San Mateo, CA (1988).
3. West, M and Harrison, J, *Bayesian Forecasting and Dynamic Models*, Springer-Verlag, Berlin (1997).

4
Applying Bayesian decision theory and catastrophe mathematics to command

In an unpublished paper [1], a simple metamodel of the military command process was constructed. The task of the commander was to achieve an objective in an efficient and effective manner. Efficiency was measured in relation to the *en route costs* involved in moving to the objective. Effectiveness was measured in terms of a *Loss function* which represented the political and military Loss involved in not achieving the objective (we shall write Loss with a capital 'L' to emphasis that it is a general negative utility concept, not just simply battle casualties). Effective and efficient solutions to this command problem then consist of solutions that minimise the overall en route cost plus the Loss involved in not meeting the objective. It was shown that such solutions sit on the surface of a cusp catastrophe. The exact position on this surface is determined by the context of the operation – specifically the time horizon of the decision, and the initial starting conditions.

In taking this approach further, we have focused on the Loss function representing the Loss in political and military terms corresponding to failing to meet the mission objective. We have discovered that significant previous theoretical work relevant to this problem has been carried out by J.Q. Smith of Warwick University, but appears not to have been exploited (at least, not in the military domain). This may have been due to the perception that applications of this approach can only be very qualitative in nature. However this is not at all the case, as we show below. There is further discussion of these issues in [2].

By now exploiting this work, we have considered a mathematical model of decision-making and military command, which is consistent with our previous research work in relation to our development of Rapid Planning as described in Chapter 2. This model is called *Bayesian decision*. In Bayesian terms it deals with the choice of a value from what is normally a posterior distribution of belief. Such decisions are arrived at by forming a distribution of belief in outcome, given that a decision is made, and a Loss function, which is a measure of the effect of this outcome relative to some goal or objective. The Bayesian decision is then the decision that minimises the expected Loss. It turns out, and can be shown mathematically, that under a broad set of assumptions concerning these Loss functions and distributions of belief, the Bayesian decision sits on a cusp catastrophe surface. As the shape parameters of the distributions slowly change, the Bayesian decision transits across this surface, and thus can change abruptly. In summary, reasonable choices of the Loss and belief distributions of the commander are likely to generate bimodal (or worse) expected Loss functions. Such a Loss function allows a smooth parameter change to lead to a discontinuous change in the decision.

This chapter gives an overview of the problem and discusses the relevance of Bayesian decision-making (and the resultant mathematics of catastrophe theory). The next chapter extends the existing theory, with a more in depth treatment of the mathematical details, and derives elegant yet simple algorithms for the further weaving together of Deliberate and Rapid Planning.

The concept of Loss

It is important to emphasise, for the work that follows, that the concept of Loss is meant to include all possible implications of not meeting the goal. This includes both military and political consequences in general.

A key outcome of the previous work [1] was the realisation that fairly natural assumptions about the decision-making problem of a commander lead, as shown by the mathematics, to the emergence of a cusp catastrophe surface representing the set of possible alternative command solutions to the problem. These alternatives correspond to different values for the constraints of the operation (specifically in that case, the time horizon available, and the starting conditions). In this way, the cusp catastrophe surface comes *after* the assumptions about the decision-making process.

The work of J.Q. Smith is most relevant to our problem and is written up in three key papers [3–5]. All of these centre around the modelling of the decision process. We shall show, by following the work of Smith, that natural and sensible assumptions about the nature of this process give rise to mathematical models that result in a cusp catastrophe surface. This is exactly what we found previously [1]. The difference here is that we focus on the Loss function due to failing to meet the objective, and neglect en route costs. This leads to a mathematical formulation that is much simpler and more straightforward. It also has direct applicability to some key aspects of command, as we shall indicate.

The mathematics of decision-making

We start off with a simple example that illustrates the general method, and which links to the discussion of Rapid Planning in Chapter 2. Consider a military commander with tactical command of a battlegroup. Within his local area of interest, one of his key concerns, we assume, is to establish a perception of the force ratio (enemy force level in the area of interest, divided by his own force level). We denote this ratio as the perceived combat power ratio (PCPR). The commander has a perception of enemy force level, which is a normal distribution with mean m and variance W. We assume that the commander knows his own force level precisely as O. The commander's belief is thus that the PCPR is normally distributed $N(m/O, W/O^2)$. For consistency with Smith's notation [4], we will denote this by $N(c, V)$.

The commander's decision problem is to decide whether to change his current perception of PCPR, given his latest sensor and intelligence reports. The value c denotes the (expected) value of PCPR on which his current posture is based. We denote the possible values of PCPR by the variable θ (again for consistency with the work of Smith [4]). We thus write:

(distribution of PCPR | no change in decision)
(= distribution of $(\delta \mid \delta) = 0 = N(c, V)$).
where δ denotes the decision that the PCPR has shifted from c to $c + \delta$.

We then set

$f(\theta \mid \delta)$ = (distribution of belief in PCPR | decision δ)
$= N(c + \delta, V)$

In order to represent the intent of the superior commander, we let μ denote a target or most desired value of PCPR, based on the overall top-down plan. (This translates into a desired mission for the battlegroup commander required by the top-down plan.)

We now introduce the Loss function, which measures the political and military cost of not meeting this desired value.

Let $L(\theta) = $ Loss due to PCPR being θ rather than the goal value μ.

As in [4], we take for $L(\theta)$ the 'conjugate normal' Loss function:

$$L(\theta) = h\left[1 - \exp\left\{-\frac{1}{2k}(\theta - \mu)^2\right\}\right].$$

The shape of this Loss function is determined by the shape parameter k, as shown in Figure 4.1.

The expected Loss associated with decision δ (that expected PCPR is now $c + \delta$) is given by:

Figure 4.1: Conjugate normal Loss function

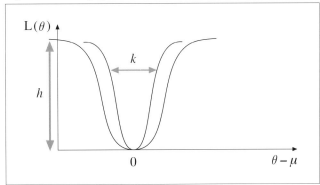

$$E(\delta) = \int_\theta L(\theta) f(\theta) \mid \delta) \, d\theta$$

$$= h \left[1 - \left(\frac{k}{k+V} \right)^{0.5} \exp{-\frac{(\delta - d)^2}{2(k+V)}} \right]$$

where $d = \mu - c$ represents the distance of the desired value μ of PCPR from the current value c, using again the notation of [4].

Assume that the Loss $L(\theta)$ changes as the magnitude of the decision δ changes, with tolerance of Loss reducing as the magnitude of the decision increases. Thus if a large change in expected local PCPR is contemplated, the consequences of getting it wrong are greater, and the tolerance to Loss is reduced.

This is achieved by making the shape parameter k of the functional form of $L(\theta)$ dependent on δ in the following way (as shown in [4]):

$$k(\delta) = (\pi^2 + \rho^2 \delta^2)^{-0.5} \tag{1}$$

The way in which this relationship changes for different values of ρ is shown in Figure 4.2.

It then follows [4] that the expected Loss, given decision (δ), which is denoted by $E(\delta)$, has two local minima, thus it has the functional form sketched in Figure 4.3. Actual plots of this relationship will be shown later.

We assume that the commander has a free choice in his decision – that is, he can choose any value of δ. The Bayesian decision is defined as that decision δ^* which globally minimises the Loss $E(\delta)$.

Figure 4.2: Relation between Loss function shape
parameter (*k*) and decision (*δ*)

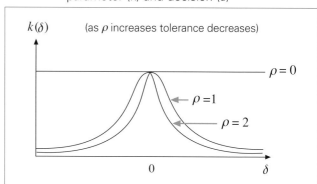

Figure 4.3: Sketch graph of expected Loss as a function
of decision (*δ*)

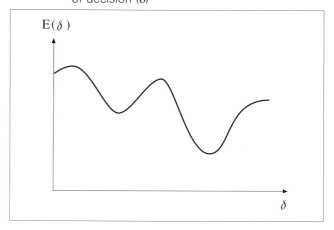

It follows from [4] that the set of all of these Bayesian decisions, which minimise the Loss function $E(\delta)$, lies on the surface of a cusp catastrophe whose control parameters are ρ (governing the relationship between Loss, and 'size' of the decision δ in equation (1) above) and d (the separation between the goal PCPR (μ) and the current PCPR (c)). Figure 4.4 shows the shape of this cusp surface as the values ρ and d are varied.

This shows the quadrant corresponding to both ρ and d being positive. Note that in this figure, the 'z axis' is the normalised value δ^*/d. This result is the direct analogy of the result obtained in [1], which showed that the optimal control solutions to the

Figure 4.4: Sketch of the surface of Bayesian decisions

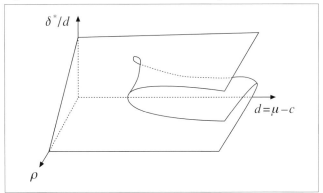

commander's decision problem, taking account of both the Loss function and the en route cost, lie on a cusp catastrophe surface which can be computed numerically, provided the various parameter values are known. What we have now shown is that if we just consider the Loss function itself, and consider the resultant Bayesian decision that minimises the expected Loss, then these Bayesian decisions lie on the surface of a cusp catastrophe. Figure 4.5 shows the projection of this surface onto the 'control' surface corresponding to the variables ρ and d. The cusp shape corresponding to the folded edges of Figure 4.4 is clearly visible.

For each of the lines drawn across the control surface in Figure 4.5, corresponding to different values of ρ, we can draw the cross-section that we would see through the cusp surface of Figure 4.4. This is sketched in Figure 4.6 (actual mathematical plots are shown in Chapter 5). The continuous line in Figure 4.6 indicates the Bayesian decision (the global minimum) at that point, the light dots indicate local maxima, and heavy dashes indicate the position of the other local minimum. Note that the Bayesian decision jumps from one sheet of the surface to the other by following the path of the global minimum. It thus jumps before the surface folds itself over. This is in contrast to the usual way in which transition is made from one sheet of the surface to the other (the Maxwell convention) where transition is made at the fold of the surface.

We can see that there are two dynamics at work. The *fast dynamic* seeks out the global minimum value (δ^*) of $E(\delta)$ for given fixed values of the shape parameters ρ and d. The *slow*

Figure 4.5: Sketch of projection onto the control surface

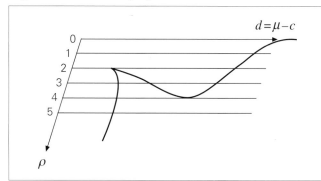

dynamic changes the value of these shape parameters and thus moves over the cusp surface, giving rise to abrupt, discontinuous changes in the decision taken. These lead in turn to changes in the CoA adopted by the commander. In the example considered here, they correspond to abrupt change from one mission to another, in order to resolve the possibly conflicting requirements of the Deliberate and Rapid Planning processes.

Implications for military command

For the example we have worked through in detail, there are a number of considerations for the military command process.

The first is that we have assumed a symmetric Loss function. This means that a Loss (political or military) is sustained if the top-down goal or objective is not attained in either direction (either below or above the objective). From discussion with military commanders, this appears most likely to happen in diplomatic/military operations where there are both political and military components to the Loss. For example, in a purely military warfighting context, if the assessment of local PCPR leads to an assignment of additional Blue force, then there will be a significant Loss if the force provided is not sufficient to carry out the mission. However, if excess force is deployed there is no, or at least a lower, immediate military penalty. Thus from a purely military point of view, the Loss function is not always symmetric.

Figure 4.6: Sketches of the cross-sections of the cusp surface

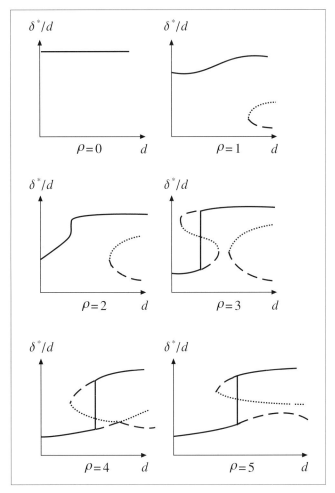

However, in diplomatic/military operations, the political and media perspectives imply that Loss functions are much more likely to be symmetric – getting it wrong in either direction has about the same level of impact. For example, if we are looking at the level of unrest in a locality during a peacekeeping operation, there may be some (low) goal level for this. Deploying forces that are too small will have political implications in terms of perceived inability to control the situation. Deploying excessive force may achieve the aim of suppressing the level of unrest, but may have political consequences such as destabilising the status quo, or appearing to take sides. Having said this, there is much work to be done to justify the shape of these Loss functions, and to consider also the case of non-symmetric Loss functions.

Walking along the graph

The emergence of the cusp catastrophe surface as the solution space for the set of Bayesian decisions $\delta*$ indicates that the graph of $E(\delta)$ in Figure 4.3 will always have at most two local minima. If the commander's decision δ is the estimate of level of unrest, or threat level, and consequent level of own force to deploy, we can trace along the path of the graph of $E(\delta)$ and form a story of what might happen in various cases.

Starting at the left-hand end of the graph, too little allocation of force leads to perceived loss of control and the expected Loss is high. At a low level of expected threat, an appropriate level of response leads to a lowering of Loss. A higher level of force deployment increases the temperature of the situation and provides additional targets, undermines the status quo and thus leads to increased political and military Loss. A further increase in force deployment (corresponding to a perception of a significant likely increase in threat) provides a deterrent, calms the situation and decreases expected Loss. Excessive deployment of force above this level leads to political problems and increased Loss.

A second implication of our analysis derives from the consideration of the shape or control parameters ρ and d. As the value of ρ increases, the value of k reduces. This means that the Loss function 'closes up' and deviations from the goal suffer larger Loss. Moving out along the ρ axis of Figure 4.4 thus corresponds to a 'blame culture' in which small errors are jumped on. In contrast, near the origin of ρ corresponds to being in 'lack of blame' where large deviations from the goal are simply shrugged off. As can be seen from Figures 4.4 and 4.6, for a given value of d, changes in ρ (the level of blame) can lead to abrupt changes in decision $\delta*$.

Similarly we can consider Figure 4.4 from the point of view of changing the parameter d. This measures the difference between the current situation c and the goal value μ. An increasing value of d can thus represent either a situation spiralling out of control (decrease in the value of c) or a progressive increase in the value of the top-down goal μ. Changing the value of d also leads to abrupt changes of decision δ^*. As Figure 4.4 shows, as the level of blame increases these changes of decision become more abrupt.

Other distributions of Loss and belief

Thus far, we have assumed a normal distribution for belief (f), and a 'conjugate normal' distribution for Loss. However, as shown by Smith [4], the theory also applies for other specified types of distribution. We discuss two of these here.

Lognormal belief and double-step Loss function

In this case, we can still think of the decision δ as being about the assessment of a particular expected value of PCPR, leading on to an assignment of Blue force, as in the example discussed. Now this value is the mean of a Lognormal distribution rather than a Normal distribution. We can also continue to think of a goal value μ corresponding to a top-down plan or requirement, and a Loss due to the assessed outcome value θ varying from this requirement. In this example the belief in the outcome θ given decision δ is assumed lognormal with median value 1, as shown in Figure 4.7. The Loss function is of 'double-step' form, as shown in Figure 4.8. Combining these together, in the same way as for the normal distribution of belief and conjugate normal distribution of Loss, leads to a cusp catastrophe surface (Figure 4.9) in which the control parameters are the coefficient of variation K of the lognormal distribution of belief, and α, which, as shown in Figure 4.8, is the level at which the double-step Loss function widens from a narrow 'well' to a broader one.

Points b and $-b$ in Figure 4.8 can be considered to be the point at which Loss goes from being *local* to being *global*. This is discussed in [4], where Smith makes the point that this form of Loss function is particularly appropriate to quality control processes. The narrow part of the well near to the goal value

Figure 4.7: Belief about future outcome using lognormal distribution

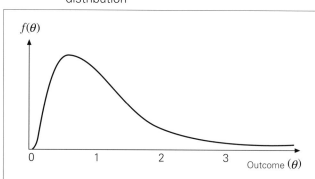

Figure 4.8: Perceived Loss

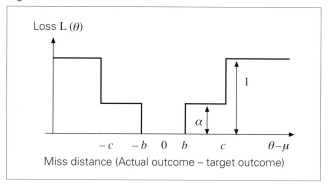

corresponds to a small Loss of 'quality' (i.e. deviation from the goal value) leading to a small Loss that can be recovered by local action (e.g. resetting the machinery and scrapping a small batch, in a manufacturing context). However, once the deviation from the goal value gets beyond a certain point (the value b in Figure 4.8) the Loss becomes much bigger – more global action is required to put things right, such as the loss of a complete order and the need for the company to process in a quite different way).

We can thus see from this that in the context of a military command process with a lognormal distribution of belief and a double-step Loss function, the control parameters of the resulting cusp catastrophe surface are related to the uncertainty of belief (the coefficient of variation K) and the relationship between perceived local and global Loss (the parameter α). These are very similar to the factors that were discussed in Chapter 2 as being likely to drive such a catastrophe process,

Figure 4.9: Surface of Bayesian decisions for lognormal
belief

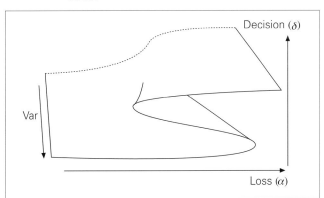

based on the psychological constructs of Janis and Mann.
However, by exploiting Smith's work, we can now put this on a
firm mathematical footing, which is a direct consequence of the
Bayesian approach to decision-making.

Pareto distribution of belief and double-step Loss function

Finally we consider the example given in [4] as a consequence
of [4], Theorem 3.3. Here, the distribution of belief (f) is a Pareto
distribution, as shown in Figure 4.10, while the Loss function L
is the double-step function as shown in Figure 4.8.

Figure 4.10: Example of a Pareto distribution of belief

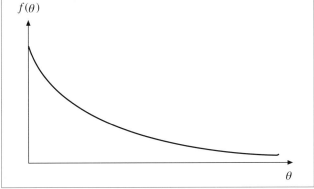

The shape of the Pareto distribution means that there is not such a natural interpretation of the 'width' or uncertainty of the distribution (although of course the variance can be defined in the usual way). However, the decision δ in the previous examples can be thought of as essentially shifting the whole distribution up or down the x axis by an amount δ, since in each case we are changing from expectation c to expectation $c + \delta$. Similarly we can think of the decision δ as shifting the Pareto distribution from a 'current' value c (corresponding to a distribution which starts at an x axis value of c, to a Pareto distribution which starts at the x axis value $c + \delta$. Smith [4] uses this approach to discuss decisions related to quality control. This might, for example, be applied to representing the performance of one or more sensors by a receiver operating characteristic (ROC) curve, with the Loss corresponding to a misclassification of a potential threat. The intelligence decision process is then dependent on minimising expected Loss in the way we have described. This example is looked at in more detail in Chapter 5.

Micro-cultures in command

Consider finally a slightly different example involving the Pareto distribution, given in [4]. We can consider a Pareto distribution which is fixed at 0 (i.e. it always starts at the x axis value 0, as in Figure 4.10) but whose shape parameter k can change. The definition of the cumulative distribution function F for the Pareto distribution in this case is given by

$$F_k(\theta) = 1 - (1 + \theta)^{-k} \text{ for } \theta > 0$$

and

$$F = 0 \text{ for } \theta < 0.$$

It follows from Theorem 3.3 of [4] that in this case, if we use a double-step Loss function, defined by values b and c as in Figure 4.8 (the c here not to be confused with the 'current value' c defined earlier) the Bayes decision δ^* is given by

$$\delta^* = c, \text{ if } 0 \leq \alpha < \alpha^*$$

and

$$\delta^* = b, \text{ if } \alpha^* < \alpha \leq 1$$

where

$$\alpha^* = \frac{F_k(2c) - F_k(b+c)}{F_k(2c) + F_k(2b) + F_k(c-b) - 2F_k(b+c)}$$

As Smith discusses in [4], we can interpret this as a polarisation of a group into two parts, corresponding to the various values α of their individual Loss functions, where α is the level at which the Loss function changes from perception of local Loss to global Loss. This relates directly to the concept of 'micro-cultures' of command discussed by Breakwell [6]. The command group can polarise into two separate groups that will take different decisions, because their perception of Loss is different.

The 'strategic corporal'

Since the value α corresponds to the level where perceived local Loss becomes perceived global Loss, we can think of two of these micro-cultures of command as exemplified by corporals in charge of checkpoints. One is sensitive to the political and military consequences of his actions, corresponding to his perception of Loss being such that $0 \le \alpha < \alpha^*$. The other corporal manning another checkpoint is not sensitive to such possibilities, corresponding to his perception of Loss being such that $\alpha^* < \alpha \le 1$. Their decisions on how to deal with particular incidents will reflect their respective perceptions of Loss, with consequences that may be global rather than local.

Summary

By exploiting the hitherto neglected work of J.Q. Smith we have considered a mathematical model of decision-making and military command that is consistent with our previous research work in relation to our development of Rapid Planning. This model is called Bayesian decision. Such decisions are arrived at by forming a distribution of belief in outcome, given that a decision is made, and a Loss function, which is a measure of the effect of this outcome relative to some goal or objective. The Bayesian decision is then the decision that minimises the expected Loss. It turns out that under a broad set of assumptions concerning these Loss functions and distributions of belief, the

Bayesian decision sits on a cusp catastrophe surface. As the shape parameters of the distributions slowly change, the Bayesian decision transits across this surface, and thus can change abruptly. This model gives direct insight into the nature and psychology of the military decision-making process, as we will discuss further in the next chapter.

References

1. Moffat, J and Witty, S, 'Changes of phase in the command of a military unit', DERA unpublished report (June 2000).
2. Fellows, R, Dodd, L and Moffat, J, 'Catastrophe theory: A review of its history and current status', DERA unpublished report (May 2000).
3. Harrison, P J and Smith, J Q, 'Discontinuity, decision and conflict', paper from Bayesian Statistics: Proceedings of the 1st international meeting, Valencia, Spain (28 May – 2 June 1979).
4. Smith, J Q, Harrison, P J and Zeeman, E C, 'The analysis of some discontinuous decision processes', *European Journal of Operational Research*, Vol. 7, pp. 30–43 (1981).
5. Smith, J Q, 'Mixture catastrophes and Bayes decision theory', *Mathematical Proceedings of the Cambridge Philosophical Society*, Vol. 86, No. 91, pp. 91–101 (1979).
6. Prins, G, 'Command in the new era', paper prepared for the Director General (Scrutiny and Analysis), MoD, UK (June 2000).

5
Extensions to the theory of Bayesian decision, and improved algorithms for resolving Deliberate and Rapid Planning[1]

As we showed in the previous chapter, catastrophe theory is a method of categorising the surfaces of the minima of continuous functions of a small number of variables, and so is a method for modelling the decision-making process. It was first developed in the 1960s by Renee Thom [1] and grew in popularity until the 1970s when the mathematical theory became well understood. At that time, scientists had not yet fully accepted its utility. Catastrophe theory was thought to be unsuitable for many applications because of the qualitative nature of the results it gave, although it can be, and is here, successfully utilised to give

---

1   The author wishes to acknowledge the key contribution of Susan Witty, Dstl Analysis, to this part of the work.

quantitative results. As discussed in [2], it was hence discarded for use in many situations in which quantitative solutions were possible.

In the case of decision-making, catastrophe theory may be utilised to put forward a simple model of the process a military commander goes through to make his decision. In the Rapid Planning process, a commander will be influenced by the naturalistic decision-making paradigm, as discussed in Chapter 2. When making a decision, he unconsciously identifies the situation that exists in the real world and applies previous experience to map this recognised situation to the most appropriate course of action (CoA). In the previous chapter we showed that this can be modelled by representing both the local and superior commanders' intents and perceptions by belief and Loss functions respectively and combining these to make up a picture of the perceived outcome Losses associated with given choices. This is the local commander's perception of the outside world. The local commander will then choose the decision which has the least expected cost associated with it. The process used to map a continuous decision onto a discrete CoA – i.e. a mission – has been previously investigated and this pattern-matching process is fully explained in Chapter 2, and in [3].

In this chapter we look in more detail at ways of using this theory to model the decisions made by military commanders. They have complex decisions to make with a number of factors to take into account, but the situation can still be reduced to a few important parameters. It should be stressed that in this case, catastrophe theory is able to give fully quantitative solutions to the problem in question. However, the values that are output are only meaningful if the functions chosen to model the circumstances correctly reflect the commanders' perceptions of the situation. Therefore, care must be taken in choosing these functions and their relevant parameters.

As described in Chapter 4, J.Q. Smith carried out research into decision-making in the early 1980s. He produced three key papers [4–6] which we use as the basis of our study into military decision-making. The chosen statistical functions represent plausible models of the commander's perceptions and are relatively simple to implement as algorithms in an agent-based combat model. These functions are chosen to reflect a commander's uncertainty in his beliefs of his current state and his potential Losses. In previous unpublished work [7], we looked at the emergence of cusp catastrophes from Loss functions that were the combination of end point and en route Loss or cost. Here, we focus on the Loss associated with the end point only, and neglect any costs originating from moving towards the end point. The Loss function is then that perceived by the unit commander due to failure to meet his objective.

The reasoning behind the theory of Rapid Planning using Bayesian decision and the mathematics of catastrophe theory has been discussed in the previous chapter. The outcome of this catastrophe theory model indicated whether the local commander should deviate from his current CoA or not. Here the theory is extended, and used to show how the understanding gained can be used to produce elegant but simple algorithms for weaving together yet further the Deliberate and Rapid Planning processes.

How does a catastrophe surface arise?

Catastrophe theory is not a single thread of theory, but is a network of ideas which encompasses many applications. The underlying principles are not mathematically complicated, although some definitions are needed before we look at the theory and its military applications and examples.

Let us consider a potential function C, in one *behaviour variable*, x. If this function is quadratic (e.g. $C(x) = x^2 + ax + b$), it will have one turning point only, as shown in Figure 5.1. If $C(x)$ is cubic (e.g. $C(x) = x^3 + ax^2 + bx + c$), it will have either two turning points – a maximum and a minimum – or one – a saddle point. If the potential function is quartic, it will have up to three turning points. The number of turning points in each case depends on the coefficients of the powers of the behaviour variable x. For example, the quartic potential function:

$$C = \tfrac{1}{4}x^4 - \tfrac{1}{2}bx^2 - ax$$

with derivative with respect to x

$$C' = x^3 - bx - a$$

Figure 5.1: Plots of functions:——, quadratic; - - -, cubic; – - – -, quartic

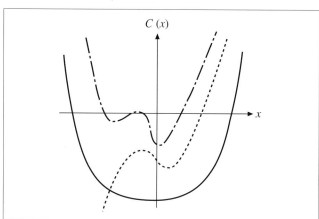

has minima when $C' = x^3 - bx - a = 0$. Now, if $a = 0$ and $b = 2$, the three turning points will be at $x = -\sqrt{2}$ (a minimum), $x = 0$ (a maximum) and $x = +\sqrt{2}$ (a minimum). However, if $a = 0$ and $b = -1$, we see that the turning points occur at $x = 0$ and $x = \pm i$. This corresponds to just one real minimum at $x = 0$.

In the cases we shall explore here, we will be interested in the minima of our potential function as we wish to minimise the expected Loss function.

The surface of the minima of the function $C(x)$ is defined as $\{x; C'(x) = 0\}$ and is known as the *catastrophe surface*. We can see that if we vary a and b we can 'walk' over the surface of the catastrophe and determine the positions of any possible folds of the surface. Therefore, a and b are known as *control variables*. If, as above, we look at a quartic potential function, the surface will exist in three dimensions and will be that catastrophe surface known as a *cusp catastrophe*. The catastrophe surface is in fact the surface $C'(x, a, b) = 0$ and can be seen in Figure 5.2.

The values of a and b can be found which bound the areas of different numbers of turning points. This set of values is known as the *bifurcation set* or *edge set*, and can be shown as the projection of the catastrophe surface on the a–b plane.

Within the area mapped out by the bifurcation set, this potential function has two minima, but both of these are not usually

Figure 5.2: The cusp catastrophe surface

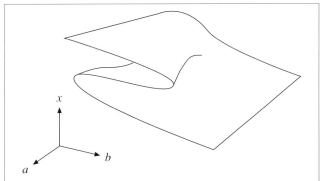

Figure 5.3: The bifurcation set

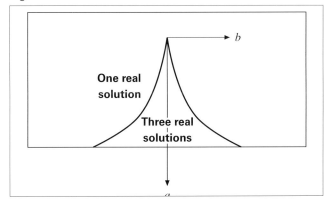

global minima. As the parameters change, the global minimum will change from one *local minimum* to the other, with an intermediate point at which both minima are equal.

It is easy to see from this discussion that the most important part of any work which uses catastrophe theory is the choice of potential function and hence the control and behaviour variables. It can be seen that, as the order of the polynomial potential function increases, the number of control variables will increase and the catastrophe surface will increase in dimension and become visually more complex. It is also possible to increase the number of behaviour variables used in the governing potential function with similar results. Thom [1] classified the elementary catastrophes as in Table 5.1.

The first two catastrophes are easy to visualise, and indeed it is the lower-dimensional catastrophes which prove the most

Table 5.1: Classification of elementary catastrophes

		Behaviour variables	Control variables	Dimension of resultant catastrophe
Cuspoids	Fold	1	1	2
	Cusp	1	2	3
	Swallowtail	1	3	4
	Butterfly	1	4	5
Umbilics	Hyperbolic	2	3	5
	Elliptic	2	3	5
	Parabolic	2	4	6

relevant to applications so we shall concentrate mainly on them in this account. The higher-dimensional catastrophes are relevant when more input parameters are used.

Current combat models

In a military decision-making scenario, the working assumption is that the unit commander will always want to take the decision δ that gives the global minimum to his *expected Loss function* based upon his past experience. He will then translate this decision into a CoA which, again, in his past experience is the most suitable. In most current OA models of combat, the decision changes are modelled by changing from one CoA to another when a threshold value of some parameter, usually the perceived combat power ratio at time t, ($PCPR_t$), is reached. One problem with using the threshold value method is that the threshold does not change according to the situation as it would in real life. If we use catastrophe theory to model the scenario, the point at which the decision change occurs is dependent upon the control variables and so the parameters in the situation. We can mark this out on the bifurcation set as shown in Figure 5.4.

As the parameters cross the dotted line, the global minimum changes from one decision to another. Therefore here, there is no threshold value, and the change of decision is dependent on some set of situation parameters (a, b).

Figure 5.4: Bayesian decision marked on bifurcation set

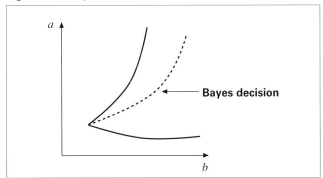

Decision parameters

In the case of a military decision, a local commander must take into consideration many different aspects of the problem. To model this decision process in the simplest possible manner, we must reduce the problem to a few relevant parameters.

The most important parameter assumed to control the situation and the commander's decision behaviour is $PCPR_t$. From intelligence and his sensors, the commander is able to give an estimate of the enemy's combat power which we assume as in Chapter 4 to have a normal distribution as output from the dynamic linear model (DLM). The $PCPR_t$ is therefore the ratio of two measures. As the commander's own combat power is usually known with almost complete certainty, and in all cases with far more certainty than the enemy's combat power, the $PCPR_t$ can be modelled as a normal distribution. Note that the intelligence and sensor information is gathered in the commander's sensor cycle, which would in general operate independently of his C2 cycle.

In Chapter 2, we discussed a set of simple discrete choices a typical land commander might have in taking a certain CoA, he may pick from a list of:

- CoA 1 = advance
- CoA 2 = attack
- CoA 3 = defend
- CoA 4 = delay
- CoA 5 = withdraw.

These five choices are valid at all levels of command for land forces and are each mapped to a range of $PCPR_t$ values as patterns with normal distributions. It is this procedure we refer to as the *pattern-matching process*.

Each local commander must decide which CoA to take based upon his current $PCPR_t$ value and the goal value of $PCPR_t$ handed down to him by his superior, which is based upon the overall top-down Deliberate plan. These two values of $PCPR_t$ may differ (and indeed they are quite likely to). It is this conflict between the superior and subordinate commanders' intentions which causes the two minima of the potential function and hence the catastrophe surface to arise, as we shall later see.

The local commander must decide whether to use his own value of $PCPR_t$ determined from his sensor reports or to use the goal $PCPR_t$ value handed down to him in his planning process. The catastrophe theory model to be described will attempt to resolve this conflict and so provide a way of modelling a local commander's decision process within the Rapid Planning context. With regard to the Rapid Planning process, the resultant output value of $PCPR_t$ can be input into the pattern-matching process to then find the associated CoA for the local commander to take.

Our question here is, how and when does the military unit commander decide to move from one CoA to another? In the following sections we shall explore various possible belief distribution and Loss functions which can be used to help to answer this question.

The belief function

Some of the factors involved when making a military decision include:

- $PCPR_t$ value
- uncertainty involved
- difference between current, preferred and ordered CoA
- maximum possible loss which could occur.

The normal distribution of $PCPR_t$ with mean c and variance V as in [5] has a density function that may be written:

$$f(\theta) = \frac{1}{\sqrt{2\pi V}} \exp\left[\frac{-(\theta - c)^2}{2V}\right] \sim N[c, V]$$

This means that the unit commander's current perceptions are that the $PCPR_t$ has a value of c with his uncertainty in this value represented by the variance value V. In a computer model of combat, c, the mean value of $PCPR_t$, could possibly be determined from the DLM as described in Chapter 2. If he were to change his accepted value of $PCPR_t$, rejecting the last reports of his intelligence and sensors, then the mean of the above distribution density would change from c to $c + \delta$ where the decision δ is the size of change in $PCPR_t$. The variance value is assumed to remain the same with the decision change. The belief in the $PCPR_t$ given a decision to change the CoA to one corresponding to a $PCPR_t$ value of $c + \delta$ is therefore given by:

$$f(\theta \mid \delta) = \frac{1}{\sqrt{2\pi V}} \exp\left[\frac{-(\theta - (c + \delta))^2}{2V}\right] \sim N[c + \delta, V]$$

This is a slight re-interpretation of the meaning of the parameter c from that in Chapter 4. Earlier, c denoted the $PCPR_t$ associated, via the pattern-matching process, with the current mission and δ, the decision that there had been a shift in $PCPR_t$. Here, we interpret the mean value c as the $PCPR_t$ value based on his sensor information and δ, the decision to change this value upon which actions are taken.

If $c = 4$ and a decision $\delta = 1$ is taken, with variance in the sensor reports being $V = 2$, the plot of $N[c + \delta, V] = N[5, 2]$ is as shown in Figure 5.5.

Figure 5.5: Distribution of belief

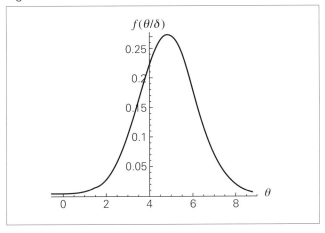

The conjugate normal Loss function

A Loss function exists which is a measure of how much a commander is 'allowed' to deviate from his superior's ordered CoA and hence ordered $PCPR_t$ value. This is a function that describes the superior commander's belief in what he thinks is the correct CoA to take. As in the previous chapter, a conjugate normal Loss function is used which means that if this method were implemented in a combat simulation model, the calculation and running time would significantly decrease relative to a general user-defined Loss function because the resulting potential function is continuous.

The conjugate normal Loss function is written:

$$L(\theta) = h \left[1 - \exp \left[\frac{-(\theta - \mu)^2}{2k} \right] \right]$$

The plot in Figure 5.6 shows $L(\theta)$ with parameters $\mu = 3$ and $h = 0.8$ for two values of k. This represents the superior commander's goal value of $PCPR_t$ according to the top-down plan, of μ. If the unit commander takes a different decision from that his superior wishes, there will be an associated Loss.

When a unit commander decides that he will change his accepted $PCPR_t$ value to something other than that corresponding to the value his sensors tell him exists, he must be

Figure 5.6: The conjugate normal Loss function

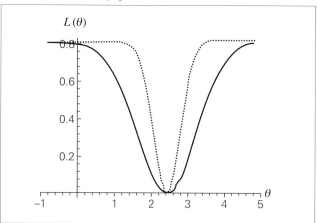

certain that it is correct. The quantity k is a measure of how important it is that the unit commander makes a correct decision. A small value of k corresponds to great emphasis placed on choosing the 'correct' decision based on the top-down plan and hence a Loss function with steep sides. A high value of k corresponds to a relaxed situation where the importance to both the local and superior commander of being in the ordered posture is lower.

The parameter h is a measure of the largest Loss that could possibly occur and is simply a scaling factor.

The expected Loss function

Multiplying the Loss and belief functions together and integrating over all values of θ gives the Loss expected if a decision δ is made. We therefore have an expected Loss function $E(\delta)$. This is our potential function as it is this quantity which we seek to minimise.

$$
\begin{aligned}
E(\delta) &= \frac{h}{\sqrt{2\pi V}} \int_{-\infty}^{\infty} \left(1 - \exp\left[\frac{-(\theta - \mu)^2}{2k} \right] \right) \\
&\quad \times \exp\left[\frac{-\theta - (c+\delta))^2}{2V} \right] d\theta \\
&= \frac{h}{\sqrt{2\pi V}} \int_{-\infty}^{\infty} \exp\left[\frac{-\theta - (c+\delta))^2}{2V} \right] d\theta \\
&\quad - \frac{h}{\sqrt{2\pi V}} \int_{-\infty}^{\infty} \left(\exp\left[\frac{-\theta - (c+\delta))^2}{2k} - \frac{(\theta - \mu)^2}{2V} \right] \right) d\theta
\end{aligned}
$$

Using a substitution of $t = [\theta - (c + \delta)/\sqrt{(2V)}]$ in the first integral and

$$
q = \left(\sqrt{k+V}\,\theta - \frac{\mu k + (\delta + c)V}{\sqrt{k+V}} \right) \frac{1}{\sqrt{2kV}}
$$

in the second integral, we obtain:

$$E(\delta) = \frac{h}{\sqrt{2\pi V}} \int_{-\infty}^{\infty} \exp[-t^2]\sqrt{2V}\, dt$$

$$- \frac{h}{\sqrt{2\pi V}} \int_{-\infty}^{\infty} \exp[-q^2]\sqrt{\frac{2kV}{k+V}} \exp\left[\frac{-(\delta-(\mu-c))^2}{2(k+V)}\right] dq$$

$$= \frac{h}{\sqrt{\pi}} \int_{-\infty}^{\infty} \exp[-t^2]\, dt$$

$$- \frac{h}{\sqrt{\pi}}\sqrt{\frac{k}{k+V}} \exp\left[\frac{-(\delta-(\mu-c))^2}{2(k+V)}\right] \int_{-\infty}^{\infty} \exp[-q^2]\, dq$$

Noting that

$$\int_{-\infty}^{\infty} \exp[-x^2]\, dx = \sqrt{\pi}$$

we find:

$$E(\delta) = h - h\sqrt{\frac{k}{k+V}} \exp\left[\frac{-(\delta-(\mu-c))^2}{2(k+V)}\right]$$

so

$$E(\delta) = h\left[1 - \sqrt{\frac{k}{k+V}} \exp\left[\frac{-(\delta-d)^2}{2(k+V)}\right]\right] \tag{1}$$

In the following, it is assumed that the unit commander unconsciously holds this expected Loss function in his head and will always pick the decision, and hence the $PCPR_t$, which minimise this function. He then maps this pattern of perception directly to a corresponding CoA, as described in Chapter 2.

To minimise the expected Loss function, $E(\delta)$, we must differentiate with respect to the behaviour variable δ and set the resulting function equal to zero. Let us set the difference between the superior's ordered $PCPR_t$, and the mean value given in the sensor cycle to be $\mu - c = d$. With h and V constant, differentiating equation (1) gives:

$$E'(\delta) = -h\frac{(\delta-d)}{(k+V)}\left(\frac{k}{k+V}\right)^{1/2} \exp\left\{\frac{-(\delta-d)^2}{2(k+V)}\right\} = 0$$

There is only one solution to this equation – a choice of $\delta = d$. The choice of mean $PCPR_t$ is then $c + \delta = c + d = (c + \mu - c) = \mu$. This corresponds to the unit commander simply taking the ordered CoA of his superior in all circumstances and ignoring the information given by his own sensors.

In real military situations, the unit commander would not always follow his superior's orders. The above solution arises because the importance of making a correct decision, k, has been set constant no matter what the decision is. Usually, if the decision made is large, it is of great importance that it is correct. If the change is small, it is of less importance. Therefore, k is dependent on the decision δ made and hence $k = k(\delta)$. We choose

$$k(\delta) = (\eta^2 + \rho^2\delta^2)^{-1/2} \tag{2}$$

So for large decisions (both positive and negative) the importance of making a correct decision is greater. As in [5], 'ρ represents a penalty for bold decisions'.

Command style representation

The constant η can be thought of as varying with the style of command that the force has. A force which has an *order-specific* command style, such as the Chinese Army example of Figure 2.4 in Chapter 2, will prefer its units to follow the superior commanders at all times and so η will be very large. This means that even a large change in decision by a subordinate unit commander will not have a great effect on the tolerance to error and k will be almost constant with the size of decision made. In contrast, a *mission-specific* command style will have a small value of η, corresponding to a style where the decisions made by the subordinate unit commander are the driving factor in the calculation of k.

Tolerance of error

The variable ρ changes as the pressures affecting the situation change. In a situation in which there is little pressure on a commanding officer to be correct, either from the outside world or his superior commander, ρ will be small as this results in larger values of k for all decisions and hence more tolerance to error. This is shown in Figure 5.7a. If there is a large amount of pressure on the unit commander to take the correct decision, then ρ will be large and therefore a small change in the decision δ will bring about a large change in value of k. The tolerance to error is small for almost all decisions, as is shown in Figure 5.7b.

Figure 5.7: Changing uncertainty with change of decision for different values of ρ: (a) a tolerant situation (small ρ); (b) an intolerant situation (large ρ).

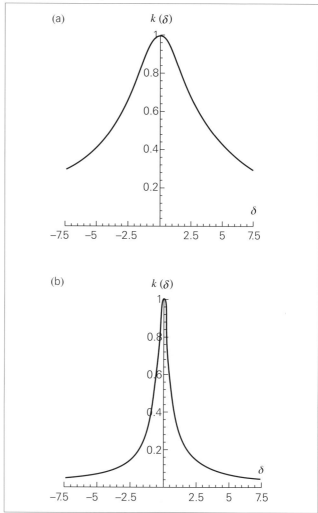

Using this definition of k in the expected Loss function gives us

$$E(\delta) = h\left[1 - \left(\frac{1}{1+V(\eta^2+\rho^2\delta^2)^{1/2}}\right)^{1/2}\right.$$
$$\left. \times \exp\left\{\frac{-(\delta-d)^2(\eta^2+\rho^2\delta^2)^{1/2}}{2(1+V(\eta^2+\rho^2\delta^2)^{1/2}}\right\}\right]$$

The analysis can here be simplified. Minimising this function would correspond to maximising the function

$$\left(\frac{k}{k+V}\right)^{1/2}\exp\left\{\frac{-(\delta-d)^2}{2(k+V)}\right\}$$

Taking logarithms of both sides of the above gives the function to maximise to be

$$\frac{1}{2}\ln\left(1+\frac{V}{k}\right) - \frac{(\delta-d)^2}{2(k+V)}$$

Maximising the above is in turn equivalent to minimising

$$\ln\left(1+\frac{V}{k}\right) + \frac{(\delta-d)^2}{(k+V)} = S(\delta)$$

Therefore $S(\delta)$ is our (new) potential function to differentiate and set equal to zero, so we have:

$$S'(\delta) = \frac{(-V/k^2)(\mathrm{d}k/\mathrm{d}\delta)}{1+(V/k)} + 2\frac{(\delta-d)}{(k+V)} - \frac{(\delta-d)^2(\mathrm{d}k/\mathrm{d}\delta)}{(k+V)^2}$$
$$= 0$$

Multiplying through by $(k+V)^2k$,

$$2(\delta-d)(k+V)k - [(\delta-d)^2k+V(k+V)]\frac{\mathrm{d}k}{\mathrm{d}\delta} = 0$$

where

$$k = (\eta^2+\rho^2\delta^2)^{-1/2}$$

(3)

and

$$\frac{\mathrm{d}k}{\mathrm{d}\delta} = -\rho^2\delta(\eta^2+\rho^2\delta^2)^{-1/2}$$

Algorithm for choice of CoA

Equation (3) looks very complicated, with a large number of variables. In fact, some of these variables may be fixed as described above, dependent on the style of the force or the particular situation. Although this requires further work, initial explanations can be found in Table 5.2. We can see from this table how we can fix certain of the variables for the situation. A commander will know how effective his sensors and intelligence are and so holds a fixed value of V. In modelling the process, this value may be obtained from the DLM as described earlier. Similarly, the measurement of command style, η, changes for different nationalities, but is fixed for a given force. This leaves us with our behaviour variable δ and the two control variables: ρ and $d = \mu - c$.

Table 5.2: Notation

Variable	Represents
δ	Decision made
μ	Superior commander's preferred $PCPR_t$ value
c	$PCPR_t$ value derived from sensor cycle
d	Difference between the two $= \mu - c$
V	Variance (and so confidence) in sensor reports
ρ	Tolerance (either of superior or external)
η	Command style measurement

If we plot the function $S(\delta)$ for various values of the control variables, we see that at certain values $S(\delta)$ has more than one minimum. The values of δ at these minima are $\delta = 0$ and approximately $\delta = d$. The first corresponds to the unit commander ignoring his superior commander's wishes and only taking into account his own sensor reports – in effect not moving from his current mission. The second corresponds to the unit commander disregarding his own sensors and simply taking the CoA his superior sets for him. The fact that the second minimum is only approximately equal to $\delta = d$ does not matter greatly as a slightly changed $PCPR_t$ value will still correspond to the superior commander's ordered CoA. This is due to the fact that the CoAs are defined as fuzzy membership functions (bell-shaped functions) of $PCPR_t$.

The plots in Figures 5.8a–c are for a fixed value of $d = 2$ and for increasing ρ. As can be seen, for low values of ρ a single global minimum exists at $\delta = d$. For higher values a second minimum

Figure 5.8a: Mathematica plots of the transformed expected Loss function, $S(\delta)$: low values of ρ, with a single global minimum at $\delta = d$

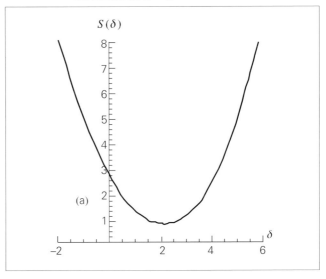

Figure 5.8b: Mathematica plots of the transformed expected Loss function, $S(\delta)$: higher values of ρ, showing a second minimum

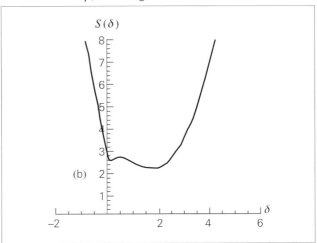

Figure 5.8c: Mathematica plots of the transformed
            expected Loss function, $S(\delta)$: still higher
            values of ρ, with a global minimum at $\delta = 0$

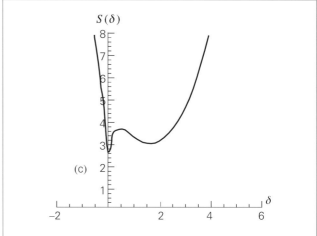

also appears at $\rho = 0$ though that at $\delta = d$ remains the global
minimum. That at $\delta = d$ becomes smaller with increasing ρ until
the minimum at $\delta = 0$ becomes the global minimum.

This behaviour can be thought of as the local commander
realising that his superior's belief or goal value of $PCPR_t$ is so
different that he no longer regards his superior's goal value as
credible at the current time and pursues his own CoA. This CoA
is derived from his belief in the $PCPR_t$ value his sensors tell him.

Although the values of V and η are fixed, they will affect the
shape of the bifurcation set. However, in general, this set will
look like the sketch in Figure 5.9. The lower right quadrant of
this sketch corresponds to Figure 4.5 of Chapter 4.

The areas in the bifurcation set can be classified by the optimum
action the unit commander can take in each area for the given
control variables. Looking at the section of the above graph for
positive ρ and d only, the areas can be classified as in Figure 5.10.
In the area circled, the decision will not take either of the
discrete values of $\delta = d$ or $\delta = 0$. However, points in this region
will in general correspond to taking the unit commander's own
preferred CoA as they will always be small since $d = \mu - c$ will
itself be small.

Figure 5.9: The bifurcation set

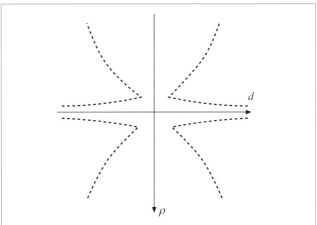

Figure 5.10: Explanation of the bifurcation set

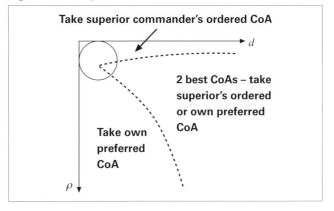

Using Mathematica, we are also able to plot 'slices' through the catastrophe surface in order to give an insight into its nature (Figure 5.11). For increasing values of ρ, the slices are plotted for different values of d. The plot to the left is that of the catastrophe surface without normalisation. The plot to the right is of the catastrophe surface of normalised minimum decisions with respect to the value d to allow comparison with the corresponding figures sketched in Chapter 4 (Figure 4.6). The solid lines in each case indicate the global minimum δ^* and the dashed line the local minimum and maximum. Cross-sections through the catastrophe surface for increasing d are shown in Figure 5.12.

Figure 5.11a: Slices through the catastrophe surface and normalised catastrophe
surface for $V = 1$, $\eta = 1$ and increasing values of ρ: (a) $\rho = 1$

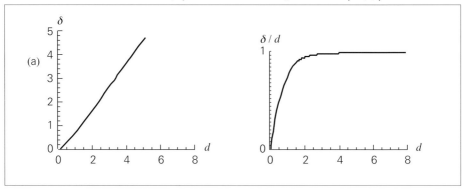

Figure 5.11b: Slices through the catastrophe surface and normalised catastrophe
surface for $V = 1$, $\eta = 1$ and increasing values of ρ: (b) $\rho = 1.5$

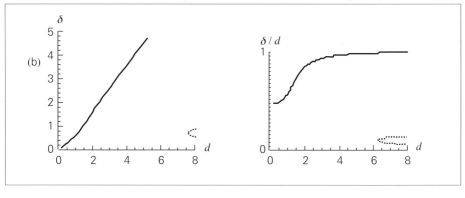

Figure 5.11c: Slices through the catastrophe surface and normalised catastrophe surface for $V = 1$, $\eta = 1$ and increasing values of ρ: (c) $\rho = 2.8$

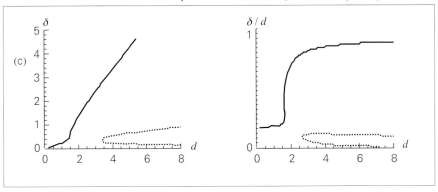

Figure 5.11d: Slices through the catastrophe surface and normalised catastrophe surface for $V = 1$, $\eta = 1$ and increasing values of ρ: (d) $\rho = 3$

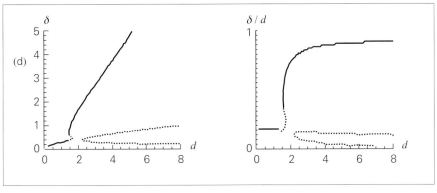

Figure 5.11e: Slices through the catastrophe surface and normalised catastrophe surface for $V = 1$, $\eta = 1$ and increasing values of ρ: (e) $\rho = 3.3$

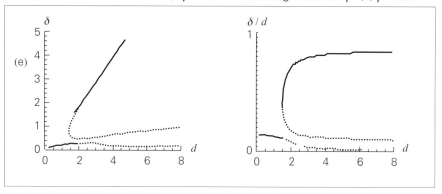

Figure 5.11f: Slices through the catastrophe surface and normalised catastrophe surface for $V = 1$, $\eta = 1$ and increasing values of ρ: (f) $\rho = 5$

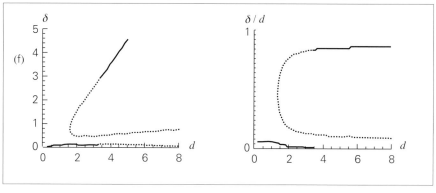

Figure 5.12: Slices through the non-normalised catastrophe surface for $V = 1$, $\eta = 1$ and increasing values of d: (a) $d = 0$; (b) $d = 1$; (c) $d = 1.4$; (d) $d = 1.45$; (e) $d = 1.5$; (f) $d = 2$.

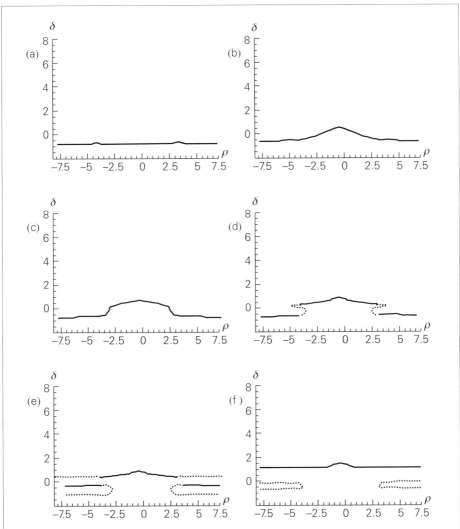

Analytic solutions

An analytic solution is not possible for our choice of $k(\delta)$ as in equation (2). If we look further into the problem, it is possible to gain a fuller insight into the mathematics by changing the choice of $k(\delta)$. If we modify our choice of k slightly and reduce our possible values of δ, we can find an analytic solution. Choosing

$$k(\delta) = \frac{1}{\alpha + \beta|\delta|}$$

and restricting our values of δ to non-negative ones only, then applying the previous methods, we find

$$S'(\delta) = \frac{V\beta}{1 + V(\alpha + \beta|\delta|)} + 2\frac{(\delta - d)(\alpha + \beta|\delta|)}{1 + V(\alpha + \beta|\delta|)}$$
$$+ \frac{(\delta - d)^2\beta}{(1 + V(\alpha + \beta|\delta|))^2}$$
$$= 0$$

Multiplying by $(1 + V(\alpha + \beta|\gamma|))^2$ means

$$(V\beta + 2(\delta - d)(\alpha + \beta|\delta|))(1 + V(\alpha + \beta|\delta|)) + (\delta - d)^2\beta = 0$$

This is a cubic equation in δ, which may be expanded as follows if we assume $\delta > 0$:

$$2\beta^2 V\delta^3 + \delta^2(3\beta + 4\alpha\beta V - 2dV\beta^2)$$
$$+ \delta(2\alpha - 4\beta d + 2\alpha^2 V - 4\alpha\beta\delta V + \beta^2 V^2)$$
$$+ (\beta d^2 - 2\alpha d + \beta V - 2V d\alpha^2 + \alpha\beta V^2)$$

Following Smith, Harrison and Zeeman [5], if we are only focusing on the $\delta > 0$ section of the E(δ) curve, it is the value of the above equation evaluated at $\delta = 0$ which is most important in determining whether a minimum occurs at $\delta = 0$. Therefore:

$$f(d) = \beta d^2 - 2d\alpha(1 + V\alpha) + \beta V(1 + V\alpha) \tag{4}$$

is the equation we are interested in. This will determine the gradient of the $S(\delta)$ curve at $\delta = 0$. For a minimum to occur, the value of equation (4) must be positive at $\delta = 0$ (Figure 5.13).

Equation (4) takes a value of zero when:

$$d = \frac{\alpha(1 + V\alpha) \pm \sqrt{\alpha^2(1 + V\alpha)^2 - \beta^2 V(1 + V\alpha)}}{\beta}$$

Figure 5.13: Sketch of $S(\delta)$

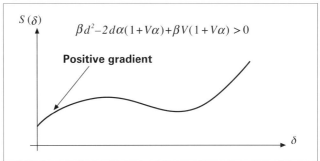

By differentiating equation (4) with respect to d, we find:

$$2\beta d - 2\alpha(1 + V\alpha) \qquad\qquad (5)$$

Equation (4) therefore has a turning point itself, at

$$d = \alpha(1 + V\alpha)/\beta$$

Differentiating (5) will tell us that this turning point is a maximum or a minimum. In fact, as the second derivative is simply 2β, it is a minimum since β is positive. The fact that our turning point is a minimum and our knowledge of the points at which equation (4) is equal to zero leads us to state that for $\delta = 0$ to be a local minimum for $E(\delta)$ the following must occur:

$$0 < d < \frac{\alpha(1+V\alpha) - \sqrt{\alpha^2(1+V\alpha)^2 - \beta^2 V(1+V\alpha)}}{\beta}$$

or

$$d > \frac{\alpha(1+V\alpha) + \sqrt{\alpha^2(1+V\alpha)^2 - \beta^2 V(1+V\alpha)}}{\beta}$$

These are indicated by the solid lines in Figure 5.14. The condition $d > 0$ is added to comply with our restriction of $\delta > 0$. This method gives us mathematical insight into how the catastrophe works, but in a military situation, and particularly for use in a simulation model of combat, our previous choice of $k(\delta)$ is more suitable, in both a mathematical and a modelling sense.

Figure 5.14: Sketch of $f(\delta)$

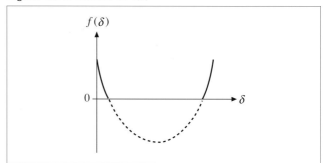

Normal belief and conjugate normal Loss functions

We anticipate that if the catastrophe model is used in a simulation model of combat to represent the local commander's decision process in the context of Rapid Planning, the catastrophe model will be run once every command and control (C2) cycle. The C2 cycle is in reality independent of the sensor cycle and hence the catastrophe decision model would be independent of the DLM cycle if this method for determining c and V were used.

The normal belief and conjugate normal Loss functions are just one choice of many that may be taken. The conjugate normal Loss function describes well a situation in which the loss perceived is continuous with changing decision. The DLM gives, as output, the belief in $PCPR_t$ gained from sensors as the mean of a normal distribution with its variance, so the two models should fit together well to give meaningful output. It is to be noted, though, that different situations require different Loss and belief functions and the assumption of normality is not suitable for the modelling of all situations.

Higher-dimensional catastrophes

The previous examples result in cusp catastrophe surfaces as they have two control variables, $(\rho, \mu - c) = (\rho, d)$ and one behaviour variable (δ). Different types of catastrophe surface arise, other than the cusp catastrophe, for different numbers of control and behaviour variables, as can be seen in Table 5.1. For the cases discussed here, and in particular, the combinations of normal belief and conjugate normal Loss functions, we look at the cusp catastrophe surface only. From Table 5.2 we can see that in the above example, V and η are taken to be constant for a given force and would be input from the DLM and fixed by the user, respectively. They may therefore be termed *fixed control variables*. However, it is possible to envisage situations where they would not be fixed, for example if the value of the variance V increased with time since the last sensor update. The parameter η, denoting the command style of the force, would also vary as the composition of the force changes, as in a coalition operation. The surface that would result if these were allowed to change would be a more complex catastrophe surface.

If one extra control variable were added, we would have a *swallowtail catastrophe* in four-dimensional space (see Table 5.1). Two extra control variables would produce a *butterfly catastrophe* in five-dimensional space. Theoretically, we could thus add extra control variables to the catastrophe potential function. However, this would increase the complexity of the situation and would therefore increase the running time when implemented in a simulation model. A balance must be struck between increased understanding and possible run time. The most important consideration must be, of course, how best to represent human command behaviour as required for our purpose. This may or may not be achieved by increasing the number of control variables. We could also increase the number of behaviour variables, resulting in an *umbilic catastrophe* (Table 5.1). This again requires further research.

The lognormal belief function

The lognormal belief function results if $\ln \theta$ is normally distributed. The distribution may be expressed mathematically as the density

$$f(\theta) = \begin{cases} \dfrac{1}{\theta\sqrt{2\pi V}} \exp\left[\dfrac{-(\ln \theta - c)^2}{2V}\right], & \theta > 0 \\ 0, & \theta \le 0 \end{cases} \tag{6}$$

This is plotted as in Figure 5.15, with $V = 1$ in each case.

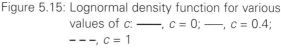

Figure 5.15: Lognormal density function for various
values of c: ——, $c = 0$; ——, $c = 0.4$;
- - -, $c = 1$

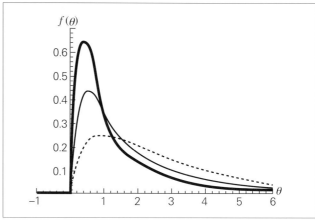

The maximum point of the lognormal density function is at $\theta = \exp[c - V]$ with

$$f(\exp[c - V]) = \frac{1}{\sqrt{2\pi V}} \exp[(V/2) - c]$$

The variance of the distribution is $(\exp[V] - 1)\exp[c - V]$. Here, we have two possible choices for the Loss function: first the conjugate lognormal Loss function and secondly the double-step Loss function introduced in Chapter 4. We shall explore each case here and give examples of how this belief function may be used in a military situation.

The conjugate lognormal Loss function

To use a Loss function, we must first specify the form the belief function must take when a decision is taken. The decision change used here for a lognormal belief function is very similar to that used in the normal example:

$$f(\theta \mid \delta) = \frac{1}{\theta\sqrt{2\pi V}} \exp\left[\frac{-(\ln\theta - (c + \delta))^2}{2V}\right]$$

This lognormal belief function can be used to describe an increase or decrease in $PCPR_t$ by a factor of θ expressed as (actual or outcome $PCPR_t$/current observed $PCPR_t$). The decision δ is then a measure of this change, whether due to the result of action being taken or simply that the observations of current $PCPR_t$ are incorrect.

The local commander will have a prior belief in the outcome if he takes no action and his sensors are correct. The maximum point of the belief function is found by differentiating $f(\theta \mid \delta)$ with respect to θ and setting it equal to zero:

$$\frac{-1}{\theta^2 \sqrt{2\pi V}} \exp\left[\frac{-(\ln\theta - (c+\delta))^2}{2V}\right]$$

$$- \frac{(-\ln\theta - (c+\delta))}{\theta^2 V \sqrt{2\pi V}} \exp\left[\frac{-(\ln\theta - (c+\delta))^2}{2V}\right] = 0$$

$$\implies -1 - \frac{(\ln\theta - (c+\delta))}{V} = 0$$

$$\implies \ln\theta - c - \delta + V = 0$$

$$\implies \theta = \exp[c + \delta - V]$$

If the commander makes no decision, the point of maximum belief is then at $\theta = \exp[c - V]$. This is the 'natural' increase or decrease in $PCPR_t$ which the local commander most strongly believes would occur if no decision and hence no action was taken. Although **V** is not the variance of the distribution as in the normal belief distribution, it can be thought of as a measure of the uncertainty in the local commander's belief that the $PCPR_t$ will change. The parameter c together with the uncertainty measure V determines the value of maximum belief if no decision is taken (i.e. that increase which the local commander believes is most likely to occur). Therefore, we would choose the value of c which gives the required point of maximum belief based on the uncertainty measure V. The decision, δ, could be positive or negative and hence will increase or decrease the local commander's outcome $PCPR_t$ with the greatest belief. The effect of the decision is to 'skew' the lognormal belief function further, but with θ still having a range of values from 0 to ∞.

We must now specify a Loss function to use with this belief function. We use a conjugate lognormal Loss function given by

$$L(\theta) = h\left[1 - \exp\left(\frac{-(\ln\theta - \mu)}{2k}\right)^2\right]$$

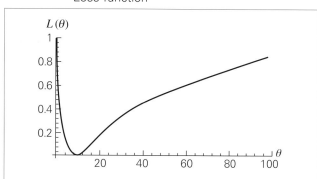

Figure 5.16: Example of the conjugate lognormal
                Loss function

with k defined as in the normal example to be $k(\delta) = (\eta^2 + \rho^2\delta^2)^{-1/2}$. This, as previously, determines the 'spread' of the loss curve. When plotted with $k = \mu = 2$, this takes the form shown in Figure 5.16. The point at which there is zero Loss is here determined only by the value μ. This point is that at which $\theta = \exp\mu$.

The Loss function is a measure of the Loss to the unit commander if he does not achieve the increase in PCPR, his superior desires or believes is the true case. Similarly, it represents the Loss if the superior commander's expected increase in enemy force levels does not occur. This is equivalent to saying the unit commander will incur a penalty if he does not achieve the aim of his action. The shape of the Loss function means that if the unit commander fails to achieve his objective and has an outcome of less than his superior commander's desired value of θ, he will receive a large penalty. If he overshoots the desired value, he will also lose, because this means his sensor cycle is not giving him accurate data. These Losses, however, will not be as substantial as for an outcome less than the desired value.

In this situation, the expected Loss function obtained is exactly that of the normal belief example of the previous section:

$$E(\delta) = h\left[1 - \sqrt{\frac{k}{k+V}}\exp\left(\frac{-(\delta - \mu - c)^2}{2(k+V)}\right)\right]$$

It is simply a result of the mathematics that the expected Loss function is identical. The plots of the transformed function $S(\delta)$

are then also identical to those considered earlier for a normal belief function.

The benefit from using the belief and Loss functions above is that they can be used to represent different situations to those represented by the normal and conjugate normal functions because the belief function is skewed and the Loss function is not symmetric. The situation discussed above is just one example. Another possible use is in the allocation of (extra) force to a mission. Both the local and superior commander will have perceptions of the 'correct' increase or decrease in force which should allocated. Here, an undershoot in force allocation might mean the mission goal would not be achieved and an overshoot would mean the mission goal was achieved, but also attracted unwanted attention and political consequences, as well as the Losses resulting from forces being taken from more useful deployment elsewhere.

The double-step Loss function

An interesting Loss function is a double-step Loss. This Loss function, together with a lognormal belief function was explored in Chapter 4. The function is written mathematically as:

$$L(\theta) = \begin{cases} 0, & |\theta - \mu| < B \\ \alpha, & B \leq |\theta - \mu| < C \\ 1, & |\theta - \mu| \geq C \end{cases}$$

and plotted in Figure 5.17 with $B = 1$, $C = 2$, $\mu = 2$ and $\alpha = 0.2$.

Figure 5.17: The double-step Loss function

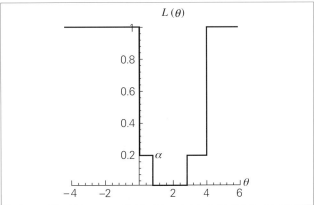

Just as the control variable, which arises from the lognormal Loss function, is ρ, the control variable which results from the double-step Loss function is α, which is the intermediate Loss.

In this Loss function, as previously, μ corresponds to the superior commander's preferred or goal ratio of outcome $PCPR_t$ to current $PCPR_t$. This Loss function corresponds to the situation in which there is a range of values of θ that will have no penalty associated with them. A further range has moderate loss and all other values will collect a maximum penalty. This type of Loss function can be used in quality control. Militarily, if we take a similar example to that used previously – the commander's preferred increase or decrease in $PCPR_t$ outcome – a superior commander may have a central goal value of outcome with an error range in which all values will be equally acceptable. A further range will not be as acceptable, but can be dealt with by local action. Any outcome not within these ranges is completely unacceptable and will attract the largest possible penalty from the superior commander – a global rather than local Loss.

The belief function, given no decision has been made, is of the form

$$f(\theta) = \begin{cases} \dfrac{1}{\theta\sqrt{2\pi V}} \exp\left[\dfrac{-(\ln\theta - c)^2}{2V} \right], & \theta > 0 \\ 0, & \theta \le 0 \end{cases}$$

The unit commander's expected belief of what this ratio will be if he takes no action is given by $\exp[c - V]$, where V is a measure of his uncertainty.

Now, let the result of the decision δ be a shift of the belief function up (or down) the θ axis by an amount δ, and define a new belief function $f_\delta(\theta)$:

$$f_\delta(\theta) = f(\theta - \delta)$$

$$= \begin{cases} \dfrac{1}{(\theta - \delta)\sqrt{2\pi V}} \exp\left[\dfrac{-(\ln(\theta - \delta) - c)^2}{2V} \right], & \theta - \delta > 0 \\ 0, & \theta - \delta \le 0 \end{cases}$$

In the previous example – the conjugate lognormal Loss function – the effect of the decision was to skew the belief

Figure 5.18: The effect of decision δ

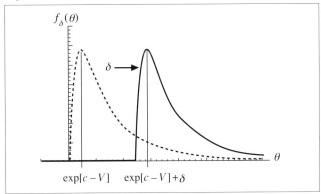

function, though still keep the range of values to be $(0, \infty)$. Here, the effect of the decision δ is to shift the belief function so that the range of possible values is (δ, ∞).

The belief function with and without a decision δ being taken can be plotted as in Figure 5.18.

Letting $\theta - \delta = X$, we can now rewrite the belief function as:

$$f(X) = \begin{cases} \dfrac{1}{X\sqrt{2\pi V}} \exp\left[\dfrac{-(\ln X - c)^2}{2V}\right], & X > 0 \\ 0, & X \leq 0 \end{cases}$$

Since we have introduced δ into the belief function we must now replace θ by $X + \delta$ in the Loss function too. This becomes

$$L(\mu - X - \delta) = \begin{cases} 1, & |\mu - X - \delta| \geq C \\ \alpha, & B \leq |\mu - X - \delta| < C \\ 0, & |\mu - X - \delta| < B \end{cases}$$

Letting $\mu - \delta$, the difference between the superior commander's desired outcome ratio and that the unit commander has decided he can achieve, be equal to D, the Loss function becomes

$$L(D - X) = \begin{cases} 1, & |D - X| \geq C \\ \alpha, & B \leq |D - X| < C \\ 0, & |D - X| < B \end{cases}$$

This, coupled with the lognormal belief function, gives a piecewise continuous expected Loss function as given below. Effectively what we have done is to change a decision that affects the belief function into one that affects the Loss function and in doing so, made the resultant mathematics far easier to manage by a simple change of variables.

- For values of $D \leq -C$,

$$E(D) = \int_0^\infty \frac{1}{X\sigma\sqrt{2\pi}} \exp\left[\frac{-(\ln X - c)^2}{2\sigma^2}\right] dX = 1$$

- For values of $-B \geq D - C$,

$$E(D) = \alpha \int_0^{D+C} \frac{1}{X\sigma\sqrt{2\pi}} \exp\left[\frac{-(\ln X - c)^2}{2\sigma^2}\right] dX$$

$$+ \int_{D+C}^\infty \frac{1}{X\sigma\sqrt{2\pi}} \exp\left[\frac{-(\ln X - c)^2}{2\sigma^2}\right] dX$$

$$= \frac{1}{2}(\alpha - 1)\text{Erf}\left[\frac{\ln(D+C) - c}{\sigma\sqrt{2}}\right] + 1$$

- For values of $-B < D \leq B$,

$$E(D) = \alpha \int_{D+B}^{D+C} \frac{1}{X\sigma\sqrt{2\pi}} \exp\left[\frac{-(\ln X - c)^2}{2\sigma^2}\right] dX$$

$$+ \int_{D+C}^\infty \frac{1}{X\sigma\sqrt{2\pi}} \exp\left[\frac{-(\ln X - c)^2}{2\sigma^2}\right] dX$$

$$= \frac{1}{2}(\alpha - 1)\text{Erf}\left[\frac{\ln(D+C) - c}{\sigma\sqrt{2}}\right]$$

$$- \frac{1}{2}\alpha\text{Erf}\left[\frac{\ln(D+C) - c}{\sigma\sqrt{2}}\right] + 1$$

- For values of $C \geq D > B$,

$$E(D) = \alpha \int_0^{D-B} \frac{1}{X\sigma\sqrt{2\pi}} \exp\left[\frac{-(\ln X - c)^2}{2\sigma^2}\right] dX$$

$$+ \alpha \int_{D+B}^{D+C} \frac{1}{X\sigma\sqrt{2\pi}} \exp\left[\frac{-(\ln X - c)^2}{2\sigma^2}\right] dX$$

$$+ \int_{D+C}^\infty \frac{1}{X\sigma\sqrt{2\pi}} \exp\left[\frac{-(\ln X - c)^2}{2\sigma^2}\right] dX$$

$$= \frac{1}{2}(\alpha - 1)\text{Erf}\left[\frac{\ln(D+C) - c}{\sigma\sqrt{2}}\right]$$

$$+ \frac{1}{2}\alpha\left(\text{Erf}\left[\frac{\ln(D-B) - c}{\sigma\sqrt{2}}\right]\right.$$

$$\left. - \text{Erf}\left[\frac{\ln(D+B) - c}{\sigma\sqrt{2}}\right]\right) + 1$$

- For values of $D > C$,

$$
\begin{aligned}
E(D) &= \int_0^{D-C} \frac{1}{X\sigma\sqrt{2\pi}} \exp\left[\frac{-(\ln X - c)^2}{2\sigma^2}\right] dX \\
&+ \alpha \int_{D-C}^{D-B} \frac{1}{X\sigma\sqrt{2\pi}} \exp\left[\frac{-(\ln X - c)^2}{2\sigma^2}\right] dX \\
&+ \alpha \int_{D+B}^{D+C} \frac{1}{X\sigma\sqrt{2\pi}} \exp\left[\frac{-(\ln X - c)^2}{2\sigma^2}\right] dX \\
&+ \int_{D+C}^{\infty} \frac{1}{X\sigma\sqrt{2\pi}} \exp\left[\frac{-(\ln X - c)^2}{2\sigma^2}\right] dX \\
&= \frac{1}{2}(\alpha - 1)\left(\mathrm{Erf}\left[\frac{\ln(D+C) - c}{\sigma\sqrt{2}}\right]\right. \\
&\quad - \left.\mathrm{Erf}\left[\frac{\ln(D-C) - c}{\sigma\sqrt{2}}\right]\right) \\
&+ \frac{1}{2}\alpha\left(\mathrm{Erf}\left[\frac{\ln(D-B) - c}{\sigma\sqrt{2}}\right]\right. \\
&\quad - \left.\mathrm{Erf}\left[\frac{\ln(D+B) - c}{\sigma\sqrt{2}}\right]\right) + 1
\end{aligned}
$$

where, as usual, $\sigma^2 = V$ and where

$$
\mathrm{Erf}(x/\sqrt{2}) = \int^x \exp(-t^2/2)\,dt
$$

As for other probability distributions, this gives a curve which can have more than one minimum for various parameters, in this case α and σ. The parameter α can be thought of as the ratio of the local to global Loss – it is the intermediate step of the Loss function. The parameter σ is a measure of the uncertainty in the local commander's belief in outcome as $\sigma^2 = V$ (Figure 5.19).

Changing the graphs in Figure 5.19 so they show varying values of σ, the uncertainty measure, rather than the intermediate step height, we obtain the plots shown in Figure 5.20.

Note that in Figure 5.19, the minima correspond to the 'step points' of the Loss function. It would be tempting to say that this is always the case, but as we see in the first of the second series of plots, the minima do not always correspond to the step points. So, the lognormal belief and double-step Loss functions exhibit two different types of behaviour, depending on the values of the other (fixed) quantities. Smith, Harrison and Zeeman [5] put forward a theorem which states the conditions for the only

Figure 5.19: Expected Loss function for $B = 1$, $C = 2$, $\sigma = 2$, $c = 2$ and changing values of local to global Loss ratio α: (a) $\alpha = 0.1$; (b) $\alpha = 0.5$; (c) $\alpha = 0.8$

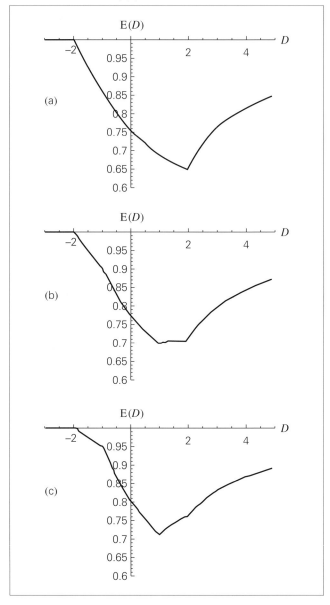

Figure 5.20a–b: Expected Loss function for $B = 1$,
$C = 2$, $\alpha = 0.5$, $c = 2$ and changing values
of uncertainty σ: (a) $\sigma = 1$; (b) $\sigma = 1.5$

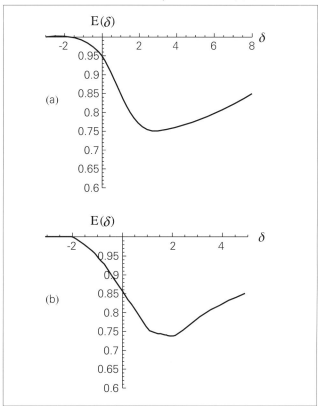

Figure 5.20c–d: Expected Loss function for $B = 1$, $C = 2$, $\alpha = 0.5$, $c = 2$ and changing values of uncertainty σ: (c) $\sigma = 1.8$; (d) $\sigma = 2$

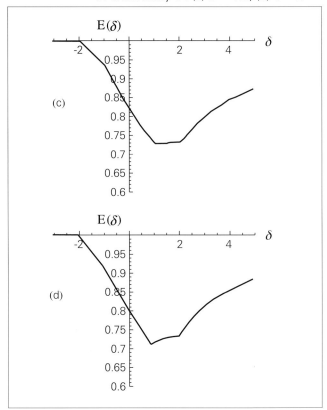

possible minima to be at the 'step points' – a double-step Loss function and a belief function which is differentiable and strictly decreasing on $(0, \infty)$ and zero elsewhere must be used. The function $\tau(\theta) = (d/d\theta)(\ln (f(\theta)))$ must also be strictly increasing on the interval $(0, 2C)$. The lognormal belief distribution is zero on $(-\infty, 0]$ and differentiable elsewhere. However it is not strictly decreasing on $(0, \infty)$ and $\tau(\theta)$ in this case is not strictly increasing. This is why the step points are not the only possible minima.

The Pareto belief function

A range of belief functions may be used in conjunction with the double-step Loss function, not only the lognormal belief function. One of the simplest is the Pareto distribution, which can be written mathematically as

$$F(\theta) = \begin{cases} 1 - (1+\theta)^{-q}, & 0 < \theta < \infty \\ 0, & 0 > \theta \end{cases}$$

with density

$$f(\theta) = \begin{cases} q(1+\theta)^{-(q+1)}, & 0 < \theta < \infty \\ 0, & 0 > \theta \end{cases}$$

These may be graphed as in Figure 5.21 and 5.22 respectively. In the Pareto distribution, the parameter that controls the shape of the belief function – the *probability density function* – is q.

Figure 5.21: The Pareto distribution function

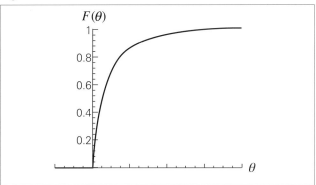

Figure 5.22: The Pareto probability density function

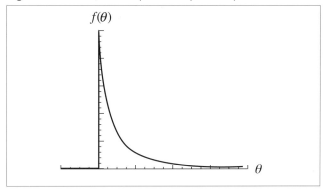

Figure 5.23: Change of decision using the Pareto belief
function: θ represents sensor reports on unit
size and $f(\theta)$ represents 'success', i.e. the
probability of size of unit as perceived by the
intelligence officer

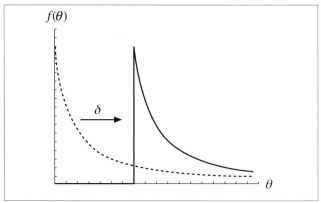

Let us explore in more detail the example put forward in Chapter 4
of the officer responsible for classifying enemy units on the
basis of incoming sensor information. He has a belief function
representing his belief in the most likely size of enemy unit he
must classify. The decision δ in this case represents whether the
officer should change this belief (Figure 5.23).

The Loss function

The Loss function is that of the double-step shown in Figure 5.17:

$$L(\theta) = \begin{cases} 0, & |\theta - \mu| < B \\ \alpha, & B \le |\theta - \mu| < C \\ 1, & |\theta - \mu| \ge C \end{cases}$$

The Loss function corresponds to the Loss resulting from a
wrong classification of enemy unit by the operating officer. His
commanding officer will hold a prior perception of the size of
the unit based on his knowledge of the current situation. This
will inform the Loss function and takes a value of μ. The stresses
upon the officer classifying the units to make the correct
decision will determine the shape of the Loss function and the
values α, B and C. A slight over- or under-estimation for the
'best' range would result in zero Loss, a larger error in

classification would result in a moderate Loss. The greatest Loss would result from a very large error in classification – for example, an enemy armoured regiment being classified as a section.

The expected Loss function

The officer responsible for classifying enemy units then models the expected Loss function and gives his optimum classification decision. Here, the expected Loss function to be minimised models the intelligence process and the sensor cycle.

As in the lognormal example, a change of variables is used. The belief function $f_\delta(\theta)$, which depends on the decision δ, can be redefined as:

$$f_\delta(\theta) = f(X) = \begin{cases} q(1+X)^{-(q+1)}, & X \geq 0 \\ 0, & X < 0 \end{cases}$$

where $X = \theta - \delta$.

Also, the Loss function, using this change of variables, becomes, as before,

$$L(D - X) = \begin{cases} 1, & |D - X| \geq C \\ \alpha, & B \leq |D - X| < C \\ 0, & |D - X| < B \end{cases}$$

where $D = \mu - \delta$.

As previously, the expected Loss function is derived by multiplying the distribution density and the Loss function together and integrating over all possible values of θ. The expected Loss function is then:

$$E(D) = \begin{cases} 1, & D \le -C \\ (1+(D+C))^{-q}(1-\alpha)+1, & -C < D \le -B \\ (1+(D+C))^{-q}(1-\alpha) \\ \quad +\alpha(1+(D+B))^{-q}+1, & -B < D \le B \\ (1+(D+C))^{-q}(1-\alpha) \\ \quad +\alpha(1+(D+B))^{-q} \\ \quad -\alpha(1+(D-B))^{-q}+1, & B < D \le C \\ (1+(D+C))^{-q}(1-\alpha) \\ \quad +\alpha(1+(D+B))^{-q} \\ \quad -\alpha(1+(D-B))^{-q} \\ \quad +(1+(D-C))^{-q}(1-\alpha)+1, & D > C \end{cases}$$

which may be plotted as in Figure 5.24 for varying values of the parameters.

Similar results are obtained for increasing q and fixed α. The possible minimum points are the points B and C of the double-step Loss function. Smith, Harrison and Zeeman's theorem [5] tells us that the minima are the step points and the global minimum or Bayes' decision, $\delta*$, is given by

$$D = \mu - \delta^* = C, \qquad \text{if } 0 \le \alpha < \alpha^*$$
$$D = \mu - \delta^* = B, \qquad \text{if } \alpha^* < \alpha \le 1$$

where

$$\alpha^* = \frac{F(2C) - F(B+C)}{F(2C) - F(2B) + F(C-B) - F(B+C)}$$

and $F(y)$ is the distribution function.

Within the context of our example here, this means that the officer responsible for determining the size of possible threats will deviate from the size of threat already perceived by either C or B, depending on how much pressure there is on him to choose correctly. However, the officer will always be cautious and choose a value less than his originally preferred value of this size, as we can see because $\delta* = \mu - D$. If there is great pressure on him to return a correct answer (a high value of α), he will return a threat size value closer to the 'preferred' size than if the situation was more relaxed, since here $\delta* = \mu - B$. If there is no great pressure on him to return a correct answer he would return a lower value, $\delta* = \mu - C$, corresponding to a value closer to that value returned by his sensors.

Figure 5.24a–c: Plots of the expected Loss function for
$B = 1$, $C = 3$, $q = 1$ and increasing values
of α: (a) $\alpha = 0$; (b) $\alpha = 0.1$; (c) $\alpha = 0.2$

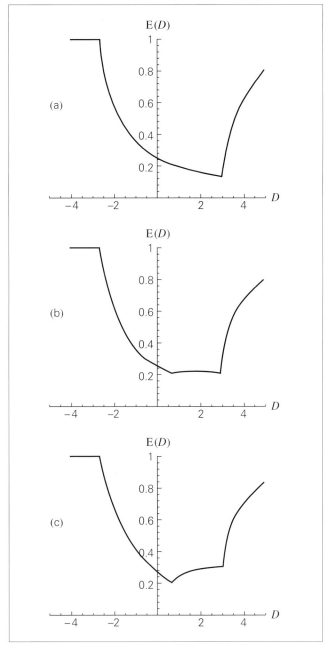

Figure 5.24d–e: Plots of the expected Loss function for
$B = 1$, $C = 3$, $q = 1$ and increasing values
of α: (d) $\alpha = 0.4$; (e) $\alpha = 1$

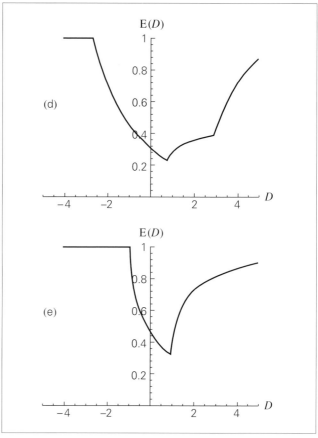

The effect of an asymmetric Loss function

Up to now, we have mainly looked at cases where the Loss functions are symmetric. In many situations this will not be so, depending on the measure of effectiveness used and whether both political and 'measurable' military Losses are used. It is important for capturing this aspect of human behaviour in applications to understand the effect of such asymmetry, and this is investigated below.

Normal belief and asymmetric conjugate normal Loss functions

The simplest problem to look at for the case of an asymmetric Loss function is an amended conjugate normal Loss function together with the normal belief function. Keeping the same notation as before, we can change the Loss function by changing the value of k depending on whether θ is less or greater than the desired value μ. Therefore the Loss function can be defined as follows:

$$
L(\theta) = \begin{cases} h\left(1 - \exp\left[\dfrac{-(\theta - \mu)^2}{2k^{(1)}(\delta)}\right]\right), & \theta \geq \mu \\[3mm] h\left(1 - \exp\left[\dfrac{-(\theta - \mu)^2}{2k^{(2)}(\delta)}\right]\right), & \theta < \mu \end{cases}
$$

which is plotted for a value of $\mu = 3$ in Figure 5.25. We can see that this describes a situation in which the local commander perceives that the superior commander would prefer undershoot rather than overshoot if an error is made.

The functions $k^{(1)}(\delta)$ and $k^{(2)}(\delta)$ can be defined by simply modifying the previous function $k(\delta)$ slightly, as follows:

$$
k^{(i)}(\delta) = (\eta^2 + A^2{}_i \rho^2 \delta^2)^{-1/2}.
$$

Figure 5.25 was plotted using $A_1 = 10$ and $A_2 = 1$.

Figure 5.25: An example of asymmetric conjugate normal Loss function

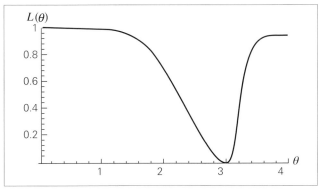

The expected Loss function which results from the Loss defined above with $A_1 = 10$ and $A_2 = 1$ is plotted in Figure 5.26 for various values of ρ together with the expected Loss functions for two symmetric Losses (equivalent to $A_1 = 1$, $A_2 = 1$ and $A_1 = 10$, $A_2 = 10$). In all cases, the bold plot is that resulting from the asymmetric Loss function.

Looking at the plots in Figures 5.25 and 5.26, we can see that the asymmetry forces the Bayes decision (the global minimum) to change at a lower value of ρ than would be seen for a symmetric Loss function with $A_1 = A_2 = 1$. It also increases the expected Loss for all values of the decision δ. However, there is no change in general behaviour.

The other control variable is the distance between the superior commander's desired value and the current value. If we increase this and plot the outcomes we obtain the graphs in Figure 5.27.

Figure 5.26a–c: Expected Loss functions from
asymmetric losses: (a) $\rho = 0$, (b) $\rho = 0.5$,
(c) $\rho = 3.5$; —— asymmetric, $A_1 = 10$,
$A_2 = 1$; ——, symmetric, $A_1 = 1$, $A_2 = 1$;
– – –, symmetric, $A_1 = 10$, $A_2 = 10$

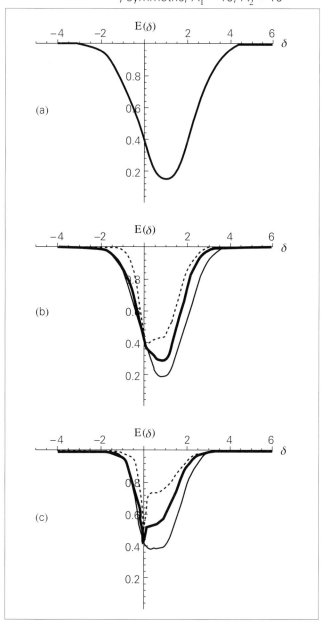

Figure 5.26d–e: Expected Loss functions from
asymmetric losses: (d) $\rho = 5$, (e) $\rho = 10$;
—— asymmetric, $A_1 = 10$, $A_2 = 1$; ——,
symmetric, $A_1 = 1$, $A_2 = 1$; – – –,
symmetric, $A_1 = 10$, $A_2 = 10$

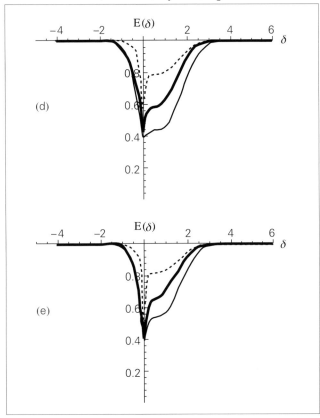

Figure 5.27a–b: Expected Loss function for increasing values of $d = \mu - c$: (a) $d = 0$, (b) $d = 0.7$; —— asymmetric, $A_1 = 10$, $A_2 = 1$; ——, symmetric, $A_1 = 1$, $A_2 = 1$; – – –, symmetric, $A_1 = 10$, $A_2 = 10$

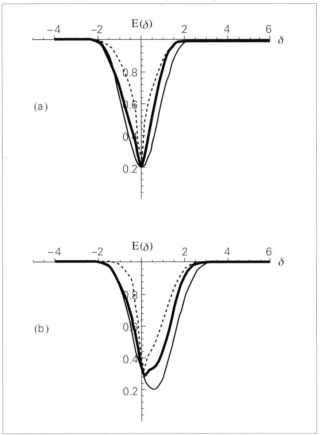

Figure 5.27c–d: Expected Loss function for increasing
values of $d = \mu - c$: (c) $d = 1.1$, (d) $d = 2$;
——, asymmetric, $A_1 = 10$, $A_2 = 1$;
——, symmetric, $A_1 = 1$, $A_2 = 1$;
– – –, symmetric, $A_1 = 10$, $A_2 = 10$

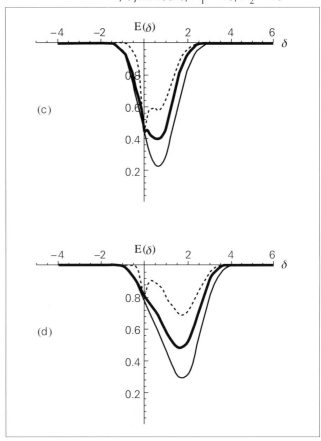

Mathematically, the expected Loss function can be written as below. We split the integration of the expected Loss function into three parts because of the asymmetry, as follows:

$$E(\delta) = \int_{-\infty}^{\infty} L(\theta) f(\theta \mid \delta) \, d\theta$$

$$= \frac{h}{\sqrt{2\pi V}} \int_{-\infty}^{\infty} \exp\left[\frac{-(\theta - (c+\delta))^2}{2V}\right] d\theta$$

$$- \frac{h}{\sqrt{2\pi V}} \int_{\mu}^{\infty} \exp\left[\frac{-(\theta - (c+\delta))^2}{2V}\right] \exp\left[\frac{-(\theta - \mu)^2}{2k^{(1)}(\delta)}\right] d\theta$$

$$- \frac{h}{\sqrt{2\pi V}} \int_{-\infty}^{\mu} \exp\left[\frac{-(\theta - (c+\delta))^2}{2V}\right] \exp\left[\frac{-(\theta - \mu)^2}{2k^{(2)}(\delta)}\right] d\theta$$

$$= h - \frac{1}{2} h \sqrt{\frac{k^{(1)}}{k^{(1)} + V}} \exp\left[\frac{-(\delta - d)^2}{2(k^{(1)} + V)}\right]$$

$$\times \left[1 - \mathrm{Erf}\left(\frac{V(d-\delta)}{\sqrt{2(k^{(1)} + V)}}\right)\right]$$

$$- \frac{1}{2} h \sqrt{\frac{k^{(2)}}{k^{(2)} + V}} \exp\left[\frac{-(\delta - d)^2}{2(k^{(2)} + V)}\right]$$

$$\times \left[1 + \mathrm{Erf}\left(\frac{V(d-\delta)}{\sqrt{2(k^{(2)} + V)}}\right)\right]$$

where

$$\mathrm{Erf}\left(\frac{x}{\sqrt{2}}\right) = \int^{x} \exp\left(\frac{-t^2}{2}\right) dt$$

The Pareto belief and asymmetric double-step Loss functions

We used a symmetric double-step Loss function to represent ranges of values which attracted the same losses. We can also define an asymmetric double-step Loss function, as follows:

$$L(\theta \mid \delta) = \begin{cases} B, & \theta - \delta \leq -w \\ \alpha, & -w \leq \theta - \delta < -v \\ 0, & -v \leq \theta - \delta < b \\ \beta, & b \leq \theta - \delta < c \\ 1, & \theta - \delta \geq c \end{cases}$$

which is plotted in Figure 5.28 for general values of b, c, v, w, α and β. A Loss function of this form would mean that an equal positive or negative difference in outcome would not always receive an equal Loss as we had assumed with the symmetric double-step Loss function. Coupling this with the Pareto belief function gives an expected Loss function which is, in general, piecewise continuous as shown in Figure 5.29 for $\alpha = \beta$ and $B = 1$. In each case, the dashed plot is that of the asymmetric Loss function and the solid plot is that of a symmetric double-step Loss function with the parameters $k = 2$, $\alpha = \beta = 0.5$, $B = 1$, $b = v = 1$, $c = w = 2$ shown for comparison in each case.

Figure 5.28: An example of an asymmetric Loss function

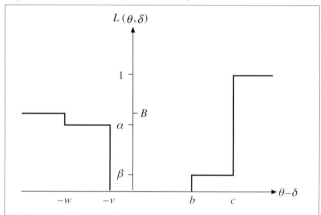

Figure 5.29a–b: Expected Loss functions: (a) $\alpha > \beta$: $k = 2$, $\alpha = 0.5$, $\beta = 0.2$, $B = 1$, $b = v = 1$, $c = w = 2$; (b) $\alpha < \beta$: $k = 2$, $\alpha = 0.2$, $\beta = 0.5$, $B = 1$, $b = v = 1$, $c = w = 2$

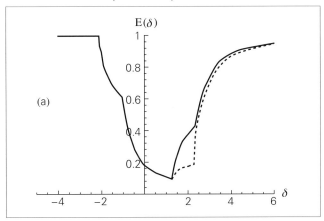

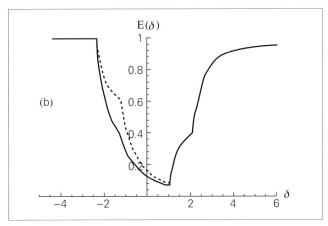

Figure 5.29c–d: Expected Loss functions: (c) $B > 1$: $k = 2$, $\alpha = \beta = 0.5$, $B = 1.2$, $b = v = 1$, $c = w = 2$; (d) $b \neq c \neq w$: $k = 2$, $\alpha = \beta = 0.5$, $B = 1$, $b = 1$, $c = 2$, $v = 2$, $w = 3$

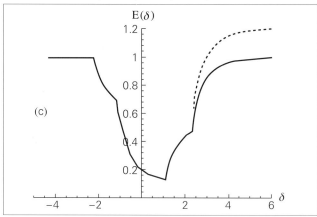

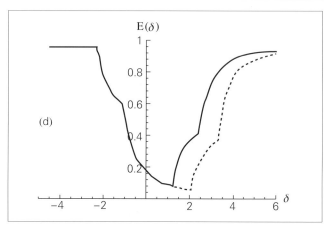

We can see from Figure 5.29 that changing the parameters of the double-step Loss function results in a modified expected Loss function. Decreasing the value of β results in a more pronounced local minimum at $\delta = c$, whereas decreasing the value of α results in the plot of $E(\delta)$ for $\delta < 0$ increasing slightly at all points. We would expect that increasing the maximum possible Loss would increase the maximum expected Loss for large decisions, and this effect is seen. Finally, changing the step points of the Loss function results in an expected Loss function that has minima at different points from the symmetric double-step Loss function. In conclusion, an asymmetric Loss will result in an expected Loss function with the same general behaviour as that resulting from a symmetric Loss function, but showing some differences in values. Similar results are obtained using a lognormal belief function.

Summary

In summary, we have shown how the use of both symmetric and asymmetric Loss functions can identify the key driving factors in the decision-making process which are consistent with the psychology of Janis and Mann. The approach emphasises the Loss due to not achieving the goal, taking account of political, media and military perspectives. It thus leads, through the decision process of the commander, to the precise use of force, consistent with modern warfare, where precision is required in position, time and effect (as shown by the recent events in Afghanistan). The mathematical algorithms developed can be incorporated into simulation models to reflect such decision-making.

References

1. Thom, R, *Structural Stability and Morphogenesis*, Benjamin, New York (1972).
2. Fellows, R, Dodd, L and Moffat, J, 'Catastrophe theory: A review of its history and current status', DERA unpublished report (May 2000).
3. Moffat, J, Dodd, L and Mason, C, 'CRP TG11 Final report on the representation of Command and Control in OA models', Vols 1–4, DERA unpublished report (March 2000).
4. Harrison, P J and Smith, J Q, 'Discontinuity, decision and conflict', paper from Bayesian Statistics: Proceedings of the 1st international meeting, Valencia, Spain (28 May – 2 June 1979).
5. Smith, J Q, Harrison, P J and Zeeman, E C, 'The analysis of some discontinuous decision processes', *European Journal of Operational Research*, Vol. 7, pp. 30–43 (1981).
6. Smith, J Q, 'Mixture catastrophes and Bayes decision theory' *Mathematical Proceedings of the Cambridge Philosophical Society*, Vol. 86, pp. 91–101 (1979).
7. Moffat, J and Witty, S, 'Changes of phase in the command of a military unit', DERA unpublished report (June 2000).

8. Janis, I L and Mann, L, *Decision-making: A Psychological Analysis of Conflict, Choice and Commitment*, Free Press, New York (1977).

6
Paths to the future[1]

In this final chapter, let us return first to the issues brought to bear in Chapter 1. The military world is indeed in the throes of a revolution: the revolution of information. The digital explosion in computation and communication technologies is bringing about structural shifts in military organisations and doctrine. Technology, and thus the modes of conflict between societies, have emerged from the agricultural and industrial ages and entered the information age. Network-centric warfare is a possible future of 'digital' war with robust networks of autonomous units, living and fighting in an interconnected environment at vastly increased tempos. Emergent behaviour is at the heart of such processes.

Modelling and analysis to determine the effect of such phenomena underpin our thinking about such future conflict, the representation of information and command being at their heart. A new approach to capturing these effects has been put forward in this book, and is having a significant influence on the approach to modelling these phenomena. However, capturing the process of intelligent agents in conflict, set within a widely divergent set of possible futures, leads to a rich set of possible trajectories of system evolution for analysis to consider. We thus need to complement this effort with other work to categorise and understand the classes of behaviours which might emerge from such a complex situation. This is the domain of complexity

---

1   I am indebted to Dr Maurice Passman of Qinetiq for his contribution to this chapter.

theory [1]. A similar point has been made by the Chief Analyst of Dstl (Roger Forder) in his discussion of the future of defence analysis [2]:

> One effect of the human element in conflict situations is to bring a degree of complexity into the situation such that the emergent behaviour of the system as a whole is extremely difficult to predict from the characteristics and relationships of the system elements. Detailed simulation, using agent based approaches, is always possible but the highly situation specific results that it provides may offer little general understanding for carrying forward into robust conclusions of practical significance. Usable theories of complexity, which would allow understanding of emergent behaviour rather than merely its observation, would therefore have a great deal to offer to some of the central problems facing defence analysis. Indeed they might well be the single most desirable theoretical development that we should seek over the next few years.

Complexity theory is an attempt to understand the structure and dynamics of real-world systems. Complexity views human systems, such as business organisations, as if they were natural organisms. In other words, it allows for the incorporation of those elements of human behaviour that 'appear' unpredictable to be taken into account. Military systems (as we have seen in earlier chapters) can be modelled as composed of diverse agents that interact with each other and with the environment. In so doing, they generate characteristic behavioural traits. These behavioural traits are not stationary. The environment is constantly changing and as a result, the system adapts and evolves. Structures of this type are defined as *complex adaptive systems* (CAS). The methodology of complexity science thus contrasts with the mechanistic, traditional perspective. Complexity science mathematically quantifies the core processes and characteristics of complex adaptive systems. In this way, we can examine, gain insight into and predict the deep nature of combat.[2]

---

[2] For a list of references linking complexity theory, its application to complex adaptive systems and the limitations of Lanchester formulations, see Illanchinski, A, *Towards a Science of Experimental Complexity*, http://www.can.org/Isaac

In this chapter, we therefore discuss the application of complexity to the problem of modelling manoeuvre warfare in a precise and realistic way. Traditionally, warfare has been modelled by using a set of coupled differential equations (Lanchester or Osipov equations), such as those linking the rate of casualty loss to the strength of the opponent's forces and a rate constant based on the efficiency of the forces involved:

$$\frac{dR}{dt} = -k_1 B(t), \qquad R(0) = R_0$$
$$\frac{dB}{dt} = -k_2 R(t), \qquad B(0) = B_0$$

where R is the Red strength at time t, B is the Blue strength at time t, and $R(0)$, $B(0)$ are their initial values.

The difficulty inherent in the development of any mechanism that describes the dynamic between manoeuvre and attrition warfare is that somewhere in the formalism such Lanchester/Osipov equations must 'fall out'. It seems a given that, somewhere in the modelling process, casualty loss is dependent in some way on the size and efficiency of the opposing force. Formally, this kind of mathematical abstraction is termed as creating a *metamodel*, which is defined as a mathematical approximation of system relationships defined by high-fidelity models or simulations. Our aim then is to create a metamodel for the kind of 'intelligent' agent-based simulation model we have described in Chapters 2–5.

We propose to start with a 'simple' system, in our case the ISAAC cellular automaton combat model, developed by the US Marine Corps Project Albert [3]. Our reason for this is that it represents an extreme point of the set of all such agent-based simulations. Why an extreme point? Because it is simple, represents the effect of local clustering of agents (i.e. local collaboration), is completely unscripted, and exhibits non-linear effects. It thus stands in contrast to the opposite extreme of a very tightly scripted model, which can only exhibit quasi-linear behaviour. We can thus think of ISAAC as the 'hydrogen atom' of agent-based simulation models. Although such a model cannot represent all the effects of flanking manoeuvres or attacks on command and control networks, other manoeuvre properties can be examined; in particular, the effects of clustering (i.e. local agent collaboration), different sensor detection ranges and movement.

Creation of a metamodel

The approach we take builds on the text by Barenblatt [4]. Firstly we have to define the fundamental set of parameters by which we characterise our system. These form a gauge class (such as mass, length, time).

Consider then, as an example, the metamodel mathematical relationship linking inputs to outputs:

$$a = f(a_1, \ldots, a_k, b_1, b_2)$$

where the arguments $a_1, \ldots, a_k$ have independent dimensions [4], and b_1, b_2 have dimensions which are expressible in terms of the dimensions of $a_1, \ldots, a_k$. It is possible to vary the arguments $a_1, \ldots, a_k$ using arbitrary positive numbers so that

$$a_1' = A_1 a_1, \ldots, a_k' = A_k a_k$$

By definition, the dimensions of a, b_1, b_2 may be represented as power monomials in the dimensions $a_1, \ldots, a_k$, for example:

$$[b_1] = [a_1]^{p_1} \ldots [a_k]^{r_1}$$
$$[b_2] = [a_1]^{p_2} \ldots [a_k]^{r_2}$$
$$[a] = [a_1]^{p} \ldots [a_k]^{r}$$

We therefore obtain the transformations

$$b_1' = A_1^{p_1} \ldots A_k^{r_1} b_1$$
$$b_2' = A_1^{p_2} \ldots A_k^{r_2} b_2$$
$$a' = A_1^{p} \ldots A_k^{r} a$$

These transformations form a group of continuous *gauge transformations* with $A_1 \ldots A_k$ as the parameters.

We now assume the *principle of relative gauge:* all physical laws can be represented in a form equally valid for all observers using gauges from the same gauge class. Our physical relationship can then be represented as a relationship between gauge transformation group invariants:

$$\Pi = \Phi(\Pi_1, \Pi_2)$$

The dimensionless invariants are given by

$$\Pi_1 = \frac{b_1}{a_1^{p_1} \dots a_k^{r_1}}$$

$$\Pi_2 = \frac{b_2}{a_1^{p_2} \dots a_k^{r_2}}$$

$$\Pi = \frac{b}{a_1^{p} \dots a_k^{r}}$$

The invariants Π_1 and Π_2 are sometimes known as *similarity parameters*. Different values of such parameters correspond to different dynamic regimes of operation of the system (an example is the Reynolds number in fluid dynamic modelling).

The metamodel function f therefore has the property

$$f(a_1, \dots, a_k, b_1, b_2) = a_1^{p} \dots a_k^{r} \Phi \left(\frac{b_1}{a_1^{p_1} \dots a_k^{r_1}}, \frac{b_2}{a_1^{p_2} \dots a_k^{r_2}} \right)$$

Three possibilities are basically available for this system [4]:

- *Type 1 metamodel.* Φ tends to a non-zero finite limit as $\Pi_2 \to 0$ or ∞. This means that Φ can be replaced by its limiting expression, with complete separation of variables, and f will be a product of powers whose values can be determined by dimensional analysis.
- *Type 2 metamodel.* Φ has power law asymptotics of the form

$$\Phi = \Pi_2^{\alpha_1} \Phi \left(\frac{\Pi_1}{\Pi_2^{\alpha_2}} \right)$$

  as $\Pi_2 \to 0$ or ∞. The power law form of the limiting expression still leads to separation of variables, but with characteristic exponents which may not all be determined by dimensional analysis (in contrast to type 1). In theoretical physics, these systems are examined from a gauge theory point of view using a renormalisation group approach in which the parameter Π_2 is considered at larger and larger (or smaller and smaller) scales (or gauges), giving an asymptotic power law expression of the form discussed.
- *Type 3 metamodel.* Neither 1 nor 2 holds and self-similarity is not observed; Φ has no finite limit different from zero and no power-law asymptotics.

For evidence of metamodels of types 1 and 2, where there is no absolute scale or gauge for the variables, this approach directs us to search for evidence of power law relationships of the form $y = x^\alpha$, which, if plotted on a log-log scale, give a straight line whose slope is the power law exponent. Such expressions arise naturally in certain types of complex systems, as shown in [1] and [4], particularly where fractal structures are involved, and are referred to as *scaling relationships*, since they have no preferred gauge or scale. Evidence of such scaling relations is thus evidence in support of the assumption of relative gauge.

Evidence for scaling behaviour

Evidence for the assumption of relative gauge should thus be in the form of scaling relationships between key variables of interest in conflict. Some of this evidence has been gathered together in [5]. Below, we briefly summarise this.

First, there is the recent work of Roberts and Turcotte [6]. By considering the intensity of the war as the number of battle deaths (suitably normalised to reflect the total civilian population), scaling relationships are obtained between the intensity of war and its frequency, which are stable over several centuries.

Secondly, Hartley [7] has analysed datasets also spanning several centuries in time. Given initial force sizes x_0, y_0 and final force sizes x, y he defines the following two dimensionless variables:

$$\text{HELMRAT} = \frac{x_0^2 - x^2}{y_0^2 - y^2}$$

$$\text{FORRAT} = \frac{x_0}{y_0}$$

In [7] it is shown that

$$\ln(\text{HELMRAT}) = \alpha \ln(\text{FORRAT}) + \beta$$

where the expected value of α is approximately 1.35 and the value of β is approximately normally distributed about the value -0.22 with standard deviation 0.7. Hartley shows that the value of α has the characteristics of a universal constant.

Finally, in [5] we considered the emergent behaviour of manoeuvre-based warfare, based on a number of sets of historical data provided by D Rowland. The historical data indicates that for a given type of breakthrough (immediate, quick or prolonged) the mean advance at breakthrough is a lognormal distribution with a certain *scaling* character corresponding to the complexity phenomenon of scaling collapse [1]. This means that all the curves collapse onto each other with suitable renormalisation of the parameters. There is also evidence from this data for two classes of such emergent behaviour, corresponding to linear and radial breakthrough. This analysis deals with the more aggregate operational level of conflict. It is complemented by recent historical analysis work at the tactical level which shows that casualties scale directly as a power law related to local force ratio [8].

Constructing a metamodel

We begin then to construct a metamodel using the formulation above. Define a metamodel in the form:

$$a = f(a_1, \ldots, a_k, b_1, \ldots, b_m)$$

where the number of metamodel parameters is given by $k + m = n$. Central to the concept of a metamodel is the ability to scale up the results of model experimentation to that of the real system. Suppose, for example, we wish to compare a physical phenomenon at full (prototype P) scale and at model (M) scale. If the physical phenomenon is the same, then, by the principle of relative gauge we have the scaling criterion [4]

$$\Pi^{(M)} = \Pi^{(P)}$$

where, if the superscripts refer to the prototype (P) and model (M) scales,

$$\frac{a^{(P)}}{a^{(M)}} = \left(\frac{a_1^{(P)}}{a_1^{(M)}} \right)^p \cdots \left(\frac{a_k^{(P)}}{a_k^{(M)}} \right)^r$$

and

$$b_m^{(M)} = b_m^{(P)} \left(\frac{a_1^{(M)}}{a_1^{(P)}} \right)^{p_m} \cdots \left(\frac{a_k^{(M)}}{a_k^{(P)}} \right)^{r_m}$$

Our core problem is to relate this scaling scheme to a metamodel formalism for the ISAAC cellular automaton combat model and also to encompass aspects of manoeuvre warfare and the effect of clustering and local collaboration within this procedure. First, let us assume that we have an agent-based conflict simulation representing the interaction between Red and Blue agents. Also assume that the command process, say for Red, is represented by the following effects:

- The number of discrete clusters of Red agents at time t, $N(t)$, is specified ahead of the simulation.
- $N(t)$ is a decreasing function of t.

The first of these effects simply suggests that we know or can calculate the average cluster size for the Red agents. The second is meant to suggest that the number of Red clusters decreases in time, reflecting the desire of Red to concentrate force. This latter assumption requires some examination. The number of Red clusters will not necessarily decrease during an ISAAC run. In many instances, the number of clusters increases due to dispersion from starting positions. Secondly, the attritional rate loss on Red will have some impact on its ability to cluster, but again, this will depend on the overall dispersion of Red during a scenario run. On the other hand, ISAAC runs that showed 'autopoiesis'[3] would probably show a decrease of the number of clusters over time.

With these assumptions, let us further assume that the smallest cluster of Red agents, $X(t)$, at time t, is taken and added to another, randomly chosen cluster of Red agents. This process thus represents both the concentration of Red force and the reconstitution of force elements. Adapting the proof in Carr and Pego [9], define

$\phi(x, t)$ = (expected number of clusters of Red agents $\geq$ size x at time t)/(initial total number of clusters of Red agents)

and

$N(t)$ = (total number of remaining clusters of Red agents at time t)/(initial total number of clusters).

---

3   Autopoiesis literally means 'self-reproduction', and expresses a fundamental
     complementarity between structure and function. More precisely, the term refers to
     the dynamics of non-equilibrium structures; that is, organised states that remain
     stable for long periods of time despite matter and energy continually flowing
     through them [3].

Given the assumptions and definitions above, it can be shown that $\phi(x, t)$, the cumulative distribution of cluster sizes at time t, approaches a self-similar distribution as time progresses. Thus the cluster size distribution evolves over time by a scaling relation. From [9], $\phi(x, t)$ can be represented in the self-similar form

$$\varphi(x,t) = \frac{g(x/X(t))}{X(t)}$$

where g is some positive continuous function and $g(1) = N(t)X(t)$. This self-similar form means that we can define the distribution of relative cluster size in a way that is time invariant (although the actual cluster sizes will change).

Now assume that the evolution of the distribution of $\phi(x, t)$ is smooth (a small change in time t leads to a small change in $\phi(x, t)$ – this is equivalent to saying that the renormalisation group is smooth [1]. If

$$\overline{\varphi}(x,(1-\delta)t)$$

is the expected cluster size x at time $(1 - \delta)t$ and

$$\overline{\varphi}(x,t)$$

is the same expectation at time t, then this assumption means we can find a constant b to first order such that

$$\overline{\varphi}(x,t) = (1+b\delta)\overline{\varphi}(x,(1-\delta)t)$$

i.e. for $\delta \rightarrow 0$,

$$t\frac{\partial \overline{\varphi}(x,t)}{\partial t} = b\overline{\varphi}(x,t)$$

thus

$$\log \overline{\varphi}(x,t) = \alpha \log t + \beta$$

and the normalised expected cluster size at time t,

$$\overline{\varphi}(x,t)$$

varies as a power law with increasing time t and scaling constant α.

This scaling scheme can be related directly to ISAAC runs and Lanchester law by assuming each automaton moves with a velocity v in time Δt. If this is the case, Lauren [10] has shown that $\Delta B/\Delta t$ is proportional to the product of (Red unit effectiveness) × (the probability of meeting a Red cluster) × (the expected number of Red units per cluster). Keeping the cluster size constant for the moment, this indicates [10] that the rate law for the ensemble average of Blue automata is given by

$$\left\langle \frac{\Delta B}{\Delta t} \right\rangle = k^{q(D)} \Delta t^{r(D)}$$

where D is the average fractal dimension of Red (and therefore an indication of how Red clusters or collaborates locally) and both r and q are exponents. This equation is a form of Lanchester law where the rate constant is dependent on the clustering of Red agents. The equation may also be seen as having Blue dependency factored into the relationships that express the probability of meeting a Red cluster. If Red cluster size varies according to a distribution $\Phi(x, t)$ and

$$\varphi(x,t) = \frac{g(x/X(t))}{X(t)}$$

where x is the cluster size and $X(t)$ the smallest cluster at time t, then we can write

$$\left\langle \frac{\Delta B}{\Delta t} \right\rangle = k^{q(D)} \Delta t^{r(D)} N(t) g(y(t))$$

where $N(t)$ is the normalised number of clusters of Red at time t and $g(y(t))$ is the scaled distribution of cluster size, whose expectation evolves as a power law (as we have shown). The above equation is thus exactly what we would expect for a metamodel of type 2. Finally, if we assume no clustering (i.e. no local collaboration between agents) then we have to replace $N(t)$ by the normalised number of Red agents at time t $[R(t)/R_0]$ and set the expectation of $g(y(t))$ to 1, producing a classical Lanchester equation of attrition warfare.

More general forms of clustering

Fundamental to the above exposition, leading to a metamodel of type 2, is the assumption that the ability of Red to cluster or collaborate locally increases with time – and thus the average number of Red clusters decreases with time. This does not adequately describe the full ability of Red to manoeuvre in a dispersed way and reconcentrate at selected points to attack Blue where necessary. Moreover, Red could begin a scenario in a 'concentrated' cluster and remain in this state throughout the whole simulation run. A more general statement of the unifying mechanism for clustering and local collaboration, leading to scaling effects and power laws is that of *self-organised criticality* (SOC).

Self-organised criticality

The SOC model of a dynamical system is derived from biological ideas of evolution. Species evolve over a fitness landscape with random mutations and relative selection towards higher fitness. Bak et al. [11] introduced a set of simple cellular automata models to describe this extremal process. (We can think of these as the simplest possible form of agent-based simulation model which represents the local interaction effects.)

Bak was able to answer two fundamental questions:

- What is the mechanism of SOC?
- What universal properties describe the system once the critical state has been reached?

In addition, Bak [11, 12] has formulated a comprehensive theory that describes the dynamics of these processes. The formation of fractal structures, the appearance of 'avalanches' whose frequency and magnitude are related by a power law relationship, and punctuated equilibria can all be related to the underlying dynamics.

In these references, two exact equations for the dynamic of self-organised behaviour have been formulated; the first describes the approach toward the critical attractor as a function of time, and is governed by a 'gap' equation for the divergence of avalanche sizes. This shows how such avalanche or clustering processes are generated. The second represents the hierarchical or fractal structure of the avalanches/clusters by describing the statistics of the number of active 'sites' or automata involved in an avalanche. An exponent governs the approach to the critical attractor state.

A number of cellular automata models of SOC are possible, corresponding to distinct types of clustering phenomena, and Bak uses a particular approach from theoretical physics known as *Reggion field theory* to relate the critical exponents in a broad range of such models to two basic exponents characterising the critical attractor. One such model captures the key idea of local clustering between physically neighbouring automata, and is known as the *Bak–Sneppen evolution model* [11].

Bak–Sneppen evolution model

In this automaton model, we have a d-dimensional lattice, and random numbers f_i drawn without replacement from the interval [0, 1] occupy the lattice sites. At each update step the extremal site (that is, the one with the smallest value of f_i) is chosen, and then it and its $2d$ immediate neighbours are assigned new random numbers. As a model of evolution, the values f_i correspond to 'fitness' values. Changing both the site and neighbouring sites captures the process of local co-evolution. It follows from [11] that the set of such active sites is a fractal in space-time (see particularly Figures 1 and 28 of that reference).

As described by [11], the approach to the critical attractor of the process (at which avalanches/clusters of all sizes are possible) is controlled by the *gap equation*

$$\frac{\mathrm{d}G(s)}{\mathrm{d}s} = \frac{1 - G(s)}{L^d \langle S \rangle_{G(s)}}$$

where $G(s)$ is the maximum extremal value $f_i(s)$ at time s, L is the linear size of the lattice, and

$$\langle S \rangle_{G(s)}$$

is the average avalanche size at time s. (An avalanche consists of a set of extremal values f_i each of which is a neighbour of the previous extremal value. The size of an avalanche is the number of time-steps for which this process continues.) From the previous equation, the rate of closure of the gap is inversely proportional to the average avalanche size:

$$\dot{G}(s) \propto \frac{1}{\langle S \rangle_{G(s)}}$$

Thus at the critical value f_c,

$$\langle S \rangle_{G(s)} \to \infty$$

and we have the scaling law

$$\langle S \rangle \approx (f_c - f_i)^{-\gamma}$$

for some exponent γ. Thus the distribution of avalanche size is governed by a power law expression at the critical point.

Before the critical point is reached, at some time t, if f_0 is the smallest random number on the lattice in the evolution model, then random numbers created at the next time-step will continue the avalanche process only if they are smaller than f_0. Thus the value f_0 can be viewed as the branching probability of a random process over time. This will give information on the avalanche size. If f_0 is a branching probability, then for larger f_0 we have larger avalanches. We thus assume [11] a scaling relation of the form

$$P(S, f_0) = S^{-\tau} g(S(f_c - f_0)^{1/\sigma})$$

to describe the probability distribution of avalanches or clusters of size S corresponding to an extremal value f_0. In the context of manoeuvre warfare, this describes the statistics of local clustering or collaboration at a transient point f_0 heading towards the critical attractor value f_c, and would replace the cluster distribution function we used previously, based on the analysis of [9]. The parameters τ and σ are model dependent and g is our scaling function. Note that the average size of the f_0 avalanche diverges as $f_0 \to f_c$, i.e.

$$\langle S \rangle \approx (f_c - f_0)^{-\gamma}$$

as we would expect from our general approach to such metamodels.

If we mark each of the minimal sites on the lattice as it is identified as an extremal value f_0, then the set of marks generated over time forms a fractal in space-time [11], as we have already noted. Cuts of this fractal in the space direction at a given time identify the site which is 'active' (i.e. chosen as the minimal site) at that time. Cuts in the time direction produce a fractal time series.

Critical systems are of particular scientific interest. Systems in critical states do not have any characteristic scale and may therefore exhibit the full range of behavioural characteristics within the particular system restraints. This means that systems at the point of criticality are in a position of optimal flexibility, in some sense. It could thus be argued that one of the requirements of military command is to so arrange things that the forces collaborate locally and thus self-organise into this optimal state.

ISAAC model examination

On the basis of the ideas developed above, we have extended the original analysis of ISAAC by Lauren [10] with the aim of developing a metamodel of that underlying complex simulation. We used mean fractal dimension D as a primary indicator of clustering in the agent combat processes, and took a representative set of ensemble distributions for each case (about 20 screen views of each simulation run). A force which is spread uniformly across the battlefield will have $D = 2$. Conversely, an extremely concentrated force will tend towards $D = 0$, which represents the force occupying a single point.

A representative set of ISAAC standard cases [3] was run and the mean fractal dimension calculated. The results were compared with those obtained by Lauren. All of the mean fractal dimensions calculated fell in the range 0.9–1.7. This is in approximate agreement with the range determined by Lauren. The cases considered by Lauren, and the additional cases we analysed, are shown together in Table 6.1. The first four cases are those calculated by Lauren [10]; the others are our own results. A regression plot of D versus q gave a slope of 0.55, which agrees with earlier analysis [10].

We have noted already that the set of all active sites (corresponding to our clustering force elements) is a fractal. It is shown in [11] that the fractal dimension of this set is given by the expression

$D(\tau - 1)$

Table 6.1: ISAAC mean fractal dimensions

Case[a]	Red fractal dimension D
Dispersed	0.7
Linear	1.7
Stochastic Lanchester	2
Recce	0.8
Dispersed	0.9
Dynamic	1.0
Fluid	1.1
Classic Fronts	1.7

[a] Requirement is for Blue to reach 25% casualty level.

where D is the avalanche/cluster fractal dimension and τ is a measure of the avalanche or cluster size distribution. For the Bak–Sneppen evolution model, which we have described above in some detail, we have $D = 2.92$ and $\tau = 1.245$ (see [11], Table II, two-dimensional case). This gives a fractal dimension for the active sites of 0.72. This fractal dimension should correspond to an optimal clustering and reclustering of the force where the links between force elements to form such clusters correspond to the steps in the formation of an avalanche in the corresponding SOC model. From Table 6.1 we see that the dispersed case (giving scope for such clustering and reclustering), comes nearest to this critical fractal value, and all other values lie above the critical value.

Linking local collaboration and control of the battlespace

As an example of how these apparently abstract ideas can give us immediate insight, in very recent work we have considered the problem of relating local force clustering and collaboration to the ability of the whole force to control an Area of Operations. Control is defined here in terms of the ability to prevent the opposing force or some third party from being able to move freely across the Area of Operations. Discussions with senior military officers confirm that the representation of such movement as a flow of fluid is a good analogy.

Let a single unit be able to control a patch of the Area of Operations (AO) corresponding to a square of side length l. We assume that the force (from our previous discussions) is clustered fractally with fractal dimension D. It follows from the definition of D that if we cut up the AO into squares of side length l, then the number of occupied squares is

$$N\ (0) = l^{-D}$$

Thus the probability of a square being under control is given by

$$p = \frac{l^{2-D}}{A}$$

where A is the area of the AO. This is in fact a standard measure of fractal clustering, and hence is a good measure of the ability of the force to locally cluster and collaborate.

We now apply a renormalisation group approach. By considering configurations in which 1, 2, 3 or 4 of the cells of side l are controlled subregions of the square of side $2l$, and assuming that control requires a span of controlled cells stretching from side to side and top to bottom (to prevent flow through the region in any direction), we have the following relationship:

$$p\ (2l) = 4p^3\ (1\text{-}p) + p^4$$

where $p(2l)$ is the the probability of control of a square of side $2l$. By continually increasing the area considered in this way, through renormalisation, we have the general iterative relationship for the probability of control at increasing levels of span of the AO:

$$\begin{aligned} p_{n+1} &= 4p_n^3(1 - p_n) + p_n^4 \\ &= p_n^3(4 - 3p_n) \end{aligned}$$

The stable points in this recursive relation then correspond to the intersection between the function

$$g(x) = x^3(4 - 3x)$$

and the line $y = x$ for values of x in the region between 0 and 1, In this region, $g(x)$ is S-shaped and it thus has three intersections with the line $y = x$. Two of these are stable, at the extreme values 0 and 1, and there is one unstable interediate point.

Interacting force units should thus polarise to either a very high level of control or a very low level of control. Any particular clustering of the force (corresponding to a particular unit probability of control p) should thus give rise to a level of control which is attracted (by renormalisation to larger areas of the AO) towards one of the two extremes.

In conclusion, in Chapter 1 we indicated why this field of enquiry is important, and in Chapters 2–5 we have set in place a way of representing the command and control process in agent-based models of warfare in the information age. In this final chapter, we have pointed the way forward to future developments based on mathematical metamodels of such processes.

In looking to future developments, our research indicates that clustering (i.e. local agent collaboration) is a key element of such metamodels. Thus we may also gain some insight into the effect of clustering and local collaboration on the emergent behaviour of the force. This lies at the heart of new concepts for command and control in the information age.

References

1. Sethna, J P, Dahmen, K A and Myers, C R, 'Crackling noise', *Nature* Vol. 410, pp. 242–50 (2001).
2. Forder, R, 'The future of defence analysis', *Journal of Defence Science* Vol. 5, No. 2, pp. 215–26 (2000).
3. http://www.cna.org/isaac
4. Barenblatt, G I, *Scaling, Self Similarity and Intermediate Asymptotics*, Cambridge Texts in Applied Mathematics, Cambridge University Press, Cambridge, UK (1996).
5. Moffat, J and Passman, M, 'Metamodels and emergent behaviour in models of conflict', OR Society Simulation Study Group Workshop, 20–21 March 2002, in press.
6. Roberts, D C and Turcotte, D L, 'Fractality and self organised criticality of wars', *Fractals*, Vol. 6, No. 4, pp. 351–7 (1998).
7. Hartley, D S, 'Confirming the Lanchesterian linear-logarithmic model of attrition', Martin Marietta Centre for Modelling, Simulation and Gaming, Report K/DSRD-263/R1 (1991).

8. Rowland, D, Poole, N P et al., 'PJHQ casualty estimation', DERA unpublished report (March 2000).

9. Carr, J and Pego, R L, 'Self-similarity in a cut and paste model of coarsening', *Proceedings of the Royal Society of London*, series A, Vol. 456, pp. 1281–90 (2000).

10. Lauren, M, 'Firepower concentration in cellular automata models – an alternative to the Lanchester approach', DOTSE New Zealand report 172 NR 1350, ISSN 1174-3387 (2000).

11. Paczuski, M, Maslov, S and Bak, P, 'Avalanche dynamics in evolution, growth and depinning models', *Physics Review E*, Vol. 53, No. 1 (1996).

12. Paczuski, M, Maslov, S and Bak, P 'Field theory for a model of self organised criticality', *Europhysics Letters*, Vol. 27, No. 2, pp. 97–102 (1994).

Index

Index by Kathleen Lyle

Printed in the United Kingdom by The Stationery Office Ltd.,
J99773   C12   06/02   19585